DOLLEY MADISON

BOOKS BY JEANNETTE COVERT NOLAN

DOLLEY
MADISON

by Jeannette Covert Nolan

JULIAN MESSNER, INC.   NEW YORK

Published by Julian Messner, Inc.
8 West 40th Street, New York 18

Published simultaneously in Canada
by The Copp Clark Publishing Co. Limited

Printed in the United States of America
Library of Congress Catalog Card No. 58—11079

For these dear young friends:
Clotilde, Eileen, Gertrude, Glad,
Helen Louise, Kate, Mary,
Ruth, Thelma and Virginia—
With love,

J. C. N.

CONTENTS

AUTHOR'S NOTE

The writer who attempts to tell Dolley Madison's story finds that it divides sharply into two parts, greatly contrasted in atmosphere and of unequal lengths. Until her marriage at the age of twenty-six to James Madison, Dolley lived in quiet obscurity, conforming to the discipline of the Society of Friends, speaking the "plain language," and wearing the plain costume of the Quakers. Thereafter, until her death, July 12, 1849, at the age of eighty-one she was the most famous woman in America, observed, admired and loved by hundreds of thousands of her fellow citizens.

Even before her death, Dolley Madison had become a legend, the subject of scores of colorful anecdotes — many of them quite untrue — that since then have persisted and often been repeated. In this book, it has been my endeavor to include only those incidents that have some reliable source of reference.

Throughout my narrative I have spelled my heroine's name as "Dolley." For this I cite Irving Brant, the discerning and scholarly biographer of James Madison. In *James Madison, Father of the Constitution (1787–1800)* Brant says:

"That name (Dolley) — the only one she ever owned, knew or used during eighty-one years — was too plain to suit early biographers. So . . . Dolley had to be Dorothea or Dorothy. The 'e' was then knocked out and the triumph of convention was complete. . . . A church official, registering births, does not write 'Dolley their daughter' if the parents have told him 'Dorothea.' Dolley herself disclaimed both of the embellished versions, as well as the spelling 'Dolly.' "

JEANNETTE COVERT NOLAN

Indianapolis, Indiana
March, 1958

DOLLEY MADISON

$$\left(\begin{array}{l}\textit{May 20, 1768}\\\textit{July 12, 1849}\end{array}\right)$$

1

SPRING IN VIRGINIA, 1783

Dolley Payne walked slowly through the grove, the skirts of her gray dress brushing the wild flowers that spread like a bright carpet at her feet. She was fifteen, tall and slender, blue eyed, with dark hair curling softly against her cheeks and neck. Her scoop-shaped Quaker bonnet was tied neatly under her chin and she wore linen gloves, but she had taken off her complexion mask, for the day was very warm.

"And a strange day it is!" she said to herself. "My last at the Cedar Creek school. To think that for the last time I'm following this old path toward home — which won't be home much longer!"

Birds were singing in the boughs of the blossoming redbud and dogwood trees, and up ahead, darting and dodging among the thickets, Isaac and Lucy were having a game of tag. Dolley smiled as she watched them. They were children, she thought,

and it was right for them to frolic and be gay. Surely this sparkling spring world was made for happiness.

Presently, breathless, they came scampering back to the path.
"Dolley!" Lucy exclaimed. "Your mask, Sister?"

"It's in my pocket," Dolley said.

"But you should have it on."

"Oh, I don't think so. I'll not get sunburned here in the
shade." Dolley pulled the oval of fine white cloth from her
pocket and dangled it by the strings. "You may be thankful that
you're just seven, Lucy, and needn't be bothered about your
complexion."

"Seven and three quarters," Lucy said. "I'll soon be eight,
you know."

Isaac was grinning mockingly. "Complexion!" he said. "Look
at me! I'm twelve, and do I bother about my complexion? Of
course not! I'm burned brown as an Injun. And freckles! —
why, I've got more freckles on my nose than I can count, and
they don't hurt a bit."

"Well, you're a boy and boys are *creatures*, Isaac," Lucy said,
regarding him with scorn. "Boys can be ugly as scarecrows, and
who cares? But pretty ladies — "

"Dolley's not a lady."

"She is! Or almost! And you can't say she isn't pretty."

"What I say is, who cares about being pretty?" Isaac wrinkled
his freckled nose. "And something else, Lucy: if I'm a creature,
you're an *imp*."

"I am not an imp!"

"Oh, yes, you are." Exploding into laughter, Isaac seized
Lucy's hand. "An imp — and I dare you to race me to the
garden gate."

"Run on, Lucy," Dolley said. "Run on, both of you, and play

while you can. Quarreling is silly, and tomorrow we'll all have to work, helping Mother with the packing."

"Not me!" Isaac's face had clouded; he scuffed the toes of his stout boots in the grass. "School's out. I'm going fishing tomorrow — and every day."

"No, Brother," Dolley said gently. "Moving our big family to Philadelphia isn't easy to do. You'll share in the task with the rest of us."

"But I don't want to move! I like Virginia and Hanover County and our farm. I'll hate Philadelphia! I don't see why we have to move, Dolley."

She smiled at him. "I think you see quite well. Father has often told us his reasons."

"Oh, certainly you see, Isaac," Lucy said. "You're only being stubborn. Come on, creature! I'll race you — and I'll win!"

When Dolley reached the edge of the grove, the children had already crossed an expanse of rolling green meadow and were scurrying pell-mell through the garden, into the house. It was a sturdy house, a large oblong of brick and clapboards, with a high hipped roof and two chimneys like enormous ears at either end. Behind it were the barns, a stable, some sheds and store-rooms, and a row of cottages which the slaves occupied. A hundred and fifty years ago this property had been the center of a pioneer settlement called Scotchtown, and the name still clung to it, though the settlement had gradually dwindled away and all that remained were these buildings, old and weathered and rather shabby.

Dolley knew that her father, John Payne, had bought the house and its surrounding farmland from Patrick Henry, who was her mother's cousin. That was in 1776, shortly after the outbreak of the American Revolution. Patrick Henry was a famous man, a leader in the struggle of the American colonists for independence from England; he had just been elected as the patriot governor of Virginia and was going to Williamsburg, the Virginia capital, to live. But John Payne was a deeply religious Quaker, opposed to war at any time — and with no intention of taking part in this one. If there was to be fighting, John Payne wanted a refuge from it, a place in which his family would be safe and undisturbed. So the Paynes had come to Scotchtown from their former home on Little Bird Creek in nearby Goochland County, and here they had lived, quiet and thrifty, during the war years.

Sometimes Dolley had wondered how her father really felt about the Revolution. Had he favored the colonists' cause? Did he exult in their victory, the founding of their new country, the United States of America? Or were his sympathies with England, the country of his ancestors?

She had wondered, but she was never to know, for John Payne never put his feelings into speech. At Scotchtown he had joined the Cedar Creek Meeting of the Society of Friends. He had read the Declaration of Independence and, faithful to his religion, had made no comment. When British raiders invaded Virginia, and were resisted and driven out by patriotic militiamen, he was silent. Though gunfire echoed in these Hanover County hills, he maintained his silence. The final battle of the war had been fought at Yorktown, not many miles distant from his house — unheeding, he had plowed his fields, planted and harvested his crops of tobacco, and supervised his slaves with scrupulous kindness.

In fact, it was the problem of slavery, not the Revolution, that

had concerned John Payne, and for him the problem was a
religious and personal one.

Like all Quakers, he believed that slavery was wrong, terribly
wrong — yet he himself was the owner of slaves, and the Virginia law would not permit him to free them. For years this had
sorely troubled him. He might have defied the law, but he knew
that if he did so, the Negroes he released would only be pursued,
arrested and returned to him. He thought that the law was aimed
chiefly at Quakers — and perhaps it was, for Quakers with their
stern views and puritanical habits were none too popular in
Virginia.

He had discussed his problem with his wife, Mary Coles
Payne, with his two oldest sons, Walter and William Temple,
and with Dolley, his oldest daughter.

"You understand that as a youth I was not a Quaker," he had
said. "My ambition then was to be a prosperous farmer. When
my father died, I inherited his slaves, and other Negroes I purchased, knowing that without slave labor I couldn't cultivate
my land successfully. But as a man I was converted to Quaker-
ism and now that I am guided by the Inner Light of conscience,
I realize that nothing is so important as obedience to the teachings of the Society. I want to be a good Quaker! — this is the
whole of my ambition. Now I pray that the law may be changed
and that I can give my slaves their freedom."

Mary Coles Payne had always been a Quaker. She thoroughly
approved of her husband's prayers. "Do you think the law will
be changed, John?" she had asked.

"There's a chance it will be," he said. "You've heard me
speak of James Madison? Madison is a man of great tolerance
and vision. His home is in Orange County, and he has held

positions of honor and influence in Virginia. When our state constitution was framed, James Madison proposed an amendment that would have given all Virginians equal religious rights — and Quakers haven't had those rights. Madison's amendment was not adopted, but I think that more and more people are seeing the wisdom of it. Yes, I am very hopeful that the law will be changed."

John Payne had considered everything that a change in the law would mean to him and to his family. He would be unable to keep his Scotchtown property and must seek some other way to earn a living.

What work could he do? And where?

"Mary," he said to his wife, "if we should decide to leave Virginia when the war is over, where would you wish to go?"

She replied: "Why not Philadelphia?"

"Philadelphia, the Quaker City? The City of Brotherly Love?"

"We know some people there, Elizabeth and Henry Drinker," Mary said. "We might send Walter to the Drinkers, to get acquainted with the city. And I could make a brief visit to them also, to see whether the place is suitable for us."

John Payne had agreed to this suggestion. Walter was sent to Philadelphia, then Mary visited the Drinkers and came back to report that the city did seem quite suitable. Months passed, while the Virginia legislators debated about changing the law, so that it might be possible for a man to free his Negro servants — anxious months for John Payne and his worried conscience. . . .

Dolley would never forget her father's expression of relief when at last he learned that the law had been changed. His stern face had relaxed into a smile as he announced that he would promptly wind up his affairs at Scotchtown and move to Philadelphia in the early summer. Dolley had felt that whatever else might happen now, her father's conscience would be soothed, and this was a blessing.

She was thinking of these things as she walked on toward the house and saw her brother Temple, tall and thin, in rough clothing and a farmer's straw hat, emerging from the stable.

"Temple!" she cried. "Wait for me!"

Temple doffed his hat and waved it, then leaned against the rail fence of the garden, waiting.

"I've made my farewells at Cedar Creek, Temple," Dolley said. "Good-by to the master, the pupils, everybody."

Temple regarded her soberly. "Were you sad?" he asked. "Did you cry?"

"Oh, no. It was rather strange and sorrowful. Farewells always are that, aren't they? But I didn't cry."

"I don't believe you ever cry, Dolley. You're brave. You and Mother are the bravest of the Paynes."

"No," she said. "Father's the bravest. Father's an example to us all."

Temple swung the gate and drew her with him into the sunny garden. In one corner, a clump of boxwood hedge had been trimmed to form a gigantic armchair. Temple hoisted himself into the chair and pulled Dolley up beside him. "This is where Cousin Patrick Henry used to lounge and cat nap," he said. "Do you remember Cousin Patrick Henry?"

She nodded. "He was here occasionally when we were just getting settled in at Scotchtown. I remember his eyes, as fierce and black as an eagle's. But he wasn't fierce at all. He would come into the kitchen and fix huge dishes of popcorn for us children, and joke with us and tell stories."

"He told us the story about the cellar underneath the kitchen," Temple said, "the dungeon, and how years ago pirates and cattle thieves were locked in it and chained and tortured until they confessed."

"I didn't quite fancy that story," Dolley said. "I've never fancied the cellar, either. Cold, damp, horrible — "

"*Haunted!* Spooks, ghosts. Brr-rr! When the wind blows a gale at night, they shriek and rattle their chains."

She laughed. "Oh, what a fib."

"I've heard them. I wonder who'll hear them after we've gone, Dolley."

"I have no idea." She looked around her, at the lilac bushes in full bloom, the bluebells, delicate anemones and pinks. A trellis of yellow cinnamon roses arched over the hedge. She broke off a sprig of the roses and tucked it into the knot of her white neckerchief. "I love the garden; it's beautiful."

"Dungeons are more to my taste," Temple said. "And you shouldn't decorate yourself with flowers. Quakers don't, you know."

"But I love flowers, especially yellow ones. Yellow is the nicest color of all, isn't it? I mean to take some slips of the cinnamon rose to Philadelphia. I'll have plenty of time for gardening there, because I'll not be going to school. Mother says that lessons in the city are very costly. Father may be able to afford them for Isaac and Lucy, but not for me."

"Well, you've had lessons enough. More than most girls your age."

"I'm not good at spelling and ciphering."

"You're not too bad, Dolley, and you write a fine, clear hand. That's enough for what you'll be doing — in the city or anywhere."

"Oh, Temple! I may do something perfectly splendid."

"Not likely. You'll probably just get married. Don't you want to get married?"

"I'm in no hurry to." She glanced inquiringly at him. "You seem very gloomy today, Brother. What's the matter?"

"It's the horses," he said. "Father sold the horses this morning. They'll be fetched away next week. The horses — and the roan colt."

"Oh, I'm sorry, Temple. The colt has been such a pet of yours."

"No, he wasn't mine, not really. He belonged to Father. I merely thought of him as mine."

Dolley was startled by the bitterness in her brother's voice. "But surely you've known that the colt would have to be sold," she said. "An animal isn't the same as slips from a rosebush. You can't put it into a trunk or satchel and load it on to a stagecoach. And the house Walter has rented for us in Philadelphia is tiny compared to Scotchtown, six or seven rooms instead of twenty."

"And not even a small barn, I suppose?"

"Walter hasn't mentioned a barn in his letters to Mother, has he?"

"I've not read Walter's letters, Dolley. They didn't interest me. We'll ride behind *hired* horses in Philadelphia, eh?"

"When we ride," she said, "which may not be often."

Temple was silent a moment; then he burst out angrily:

"Father's selling everything. The fields, the crops growing in them, the farm implements and stock — everything! And at a sacrifice, for much less than it's worth."

"But Father doesn't think of it so, in terms of money," Dolley said, "and *we* mustn't. Let's think of how new and exciting city life will be. You've never seen a city, Temple; no, nor have I — "

"I've never wanted to see a city!"

"But aren't you in the least curious?"

"Not in the least," he said bluntly. "I'm a farmer, exactly as Father is. I've been content with my lot."

"Well, perhaps later you can come back to farming."

"I will!" Temple frowned. "Dolley, we'll be lonely in Philadelphia?"

"Lonely? Oh, no. The Drinkers will introduce us to other Friends, we'll join their Meeting. Walter says there are two Drinker girls, Nancy and Sally, very nice girls — "

"We'll be *poor*."

"But we've never been rich, Temple. Scotchtown was never one of the great rich Virginia plantations, not even in Cousin Patrick Henry's time."

"I think our life here has been comfortable and just right."

Dolley paused. Yes, their life at Scotchtown had been comfortable — but so uneventful, so isolated. No excursions except for the First Day meetings at Cedar Creek, no diversions except a traveler's passing once or twice in the year, a relative dropping in to spend the night. Dolley had dreamed of a larger, more satisfying world; she was puzzled by Temple's mood of black depression.

"Why must you imagine that we'll be poor in Philadelphia?" she asked. "Father will have some sort of business."

"Father will be a businessman, a merchant, Dolley. And I'll be a town fellow, a clerk — as Walter is, already."

"When I think of the city," she said, "it's of the markets and theaters. The shops with shelves of goods imported from Europe, Asia, the Orient. Crowded streets and carriages rumbling by; ladies dressed in rainbow silks, gentlemen in frilled waistcoats, knee breeches and silver-buckled shoes. Parades, Christmas and Easter celebrations — "

"Dolley!" Temple stared at her, aghast. "Are you crazy, Dolley? Theaters, rainbow silks, celebrations!"

"Oh, I know those things aren't for me — "

"Or for any Quaker."

She smiled. "No, I'm thinking of them for other people that I've read about — people who dance and sing and go to balls. I've wished that I could sing! And I *would*, if our Quaker discipline didn't forbid it. What's the harm in music? You say you're not curious, Temple. I am! I love adventures — "

"You've never had an adventure. Not one!"

"That's just it!" she said. "Philadelphia will be an adventure."

"My dear sister, you're crazy as a loon." Temple shook his head. He got down from the hedge and stretched his long legs. "Well, I've chores to do. Now that the Negroes are leaving, I have a few more chores each day."

"And I have to help Amy with supper." Dolley slid to the ground. She straightened her gray skirts. "Are Father and Mother still working at the manumission papers?"

"They were at noon. I suppose Amy will be the last of the servants to leave. When does she go?"

"I don't know," Dolley said. "Soon, probably."

"You'll dread that farewell, won't you?"

"Yes, awfully. But there's no remedy for it."

Temple made a wry face. "You're determined to be cheerful."

"And you're determined to be gloomy," she retorted. "You and Isaac are a pair. I'd like to spank you both."

"Oh, I daresay." He turned toward the barn, then added: "Have you planned how you'll stuff the ten Paynes into Walter's tiny house on your crowded street? Crowded and *noisy*. It'll take a deal of cramming to get us all in. We'll be tight as salt codfish in a barrel."

"Not tight, just cozy."

"Dolley, why do you pretend so?"

"I'm not pretending. You know I never pretend," she said. "But I wish you'd pretend a bit. It does seem to me, Temple, that if things can't be remedied, we'd better be cheerful about them."

"Now you're scolding me!"

"Yes. I realize that it isn't easy for you to give up the colt, the horses, many things you're fond of. You're disappointed, and I'm not blaming you for that. But I think you should hide your feelings — from Father, anyway; for his sake. Because Father *is* making a sacrifice, a great sacrifice, and we mustn't spoil it. Won't you *try* to be sweet, Temple?"

"Sweet?" he repeated. "Bosh! . . . Oh, well, all right. I'll try. I'll grin like a crocodile — even though it kills me."

"It won't," Dolley said. "I honestly don't believe that grinning ever killed anybody."

2

IMPORTANT PAPERS

When Dolley entered the kitchen slanting rays of four o'clock sunshine were gilding the windows and embers glowed dimly on the flagstone hearth. Copper kettles glinted on the cranes, the pine floor had been freshly scrubbed. Lucy sat at the trestle table, perched on a stool, a blue china bowl and a pewter spoon in her hands. Securely tied into a high chair was a plump, blond-haired baby boy. Lucy was feeding the baby mush from the bowl. She looked up at Dolley and flourished the spoon.

"I did win the race," she said. "Isaac fusses and boasts, but he's slow as molasses. I can always beat him running."

Dolley hung her bonnet on a peg in the cupboard and got out her apron. "Where is Isaac now?" she asked.

"He went to gather the eggs — with Anna and Mary trotting after him. *Those* infants!" Lucy said. "I'd have chased them, but the minute Amy saw me, she grabbed me and said I had to tend Johnnie for her."

"Dear Johnnie," Dolley said, stooping to kiss the baby on the cheek. "Little angel!"

"Little pig!" Lucy exclaimed. "Johnnie gobbles. He has the most *tremenjous* appetite and a hollow stomach. And see how he dribbles this mush — all over him."

Dolley put on her apron. "And where is Amy?"

"In the parlor. She said Father wanted to talk to her about her manumission paper. I think Father and Mother have nearly finished with the papers. They must be dog tired of writing."

"The papers are legal documents and have to be written correctly," Dolley said. "Every slave that Father frees will have a paper to show that from now on he *is* free, and can never again be bought or sold on the auction block. That's the meaning of the word 'manumit' — to free from slavery. The names of the Negroes are on their papers, and why they've been released and other information. Each document has to be signed. Mother makes copies of them, a copy for Father, and one for the government records at Williamsburg. Then Father seals them. It's very tedious work."

Lucy lifted the baby's bib and wiped his dimpled chin. "I wish Father didn't feel that Amy should be manumitted," she said ruefully.

"Well, he does feel so."

"I love Amy. She's the oldest servant we have. She's been with us *forever*, and nursed all of us. I just love her — and I don't see how we'll get along without her — "

"Oh, Lucy, don't *you* begin that!"

"Begin what?" Lucy's eyes were wide and innocent. "Why are you cross at me?"

"Never mind," Dolley said quickly. "I'm sorry. Of course, we all love Amy and we'll miss her awfully."

Lucy scraped the bowl and fed the last spoonful of mush to the baby. "*Good* little pig," she murmured, and patted his head. "Dolley, guess what Amy told me? She said that when Father gives her the paper, she intends to jog his memory about something he seems to have forgotten. She scowled when she said it."

"Scowled? Surely not! I may be out of temper, but Amy never is."

"It wasn't a cross scowl, just — well, *broody*. Dolley, what in creation could she have to say to Father?"

"I'm going to the parlor to ask Mother about supper. Perhaps I'll hear."

"And will you tell me?"

"Perhaps," Dolley said. "Unless it's something I shouldn't."

She went through the hall to the parlor door and paused on the threshold. The parlor was the largest of the twenty large rooms in the Scotchtown house; the Paynes referred to it as the "keeping room." The walls were paneled in dark oak. Stiff-backed chairs were ranged in a crescent to face the black marble mantel, for it was John Payne's custom on winter evenings to assemble his family and servants here and to read aloud to them from the Bible. Today these chairs had been shifted somewhat from their usual positions. A big desk had been dragged to the middle of the floor. Both John Payne and his wife were sitting at the desk, on which were tidy stacks of papers, quill pens, inkhorns and shakers of blotting sand. A candle burned in a shallow saucer, the pleasing fragrance of sealing wax drifted in the air. Close by sat Amy, an elderly Negro woman, immaculate in her bandanna turban and neat print dress.

Dolley saw that her mother had looked up and raised a warning finger, as if for silence. Dolley sat down on a chair near the door. The scratching of John Payne's pen was the only sound in the room. It was like a picture, Dolley thought, so hushed, her father's profile so severe above the paper on which he wrote, her mother's attitude of calm repose — and Amy, erect and dignified, her eyes fixed on that swift-gliding pen.

John Payne thrust the pen aside, sanded and folded the sheet of paper, and melted a stick of red wax in the candle's flame. Hot beads of wax dripped onto the paper, making a seal. When the wax had cooled, he held the paper out to Amy.

"You know what this document is, Amy?" he said.

"Yes, master." She glanced at the paper, but did not touch it.

"Don't call me 'master;' you're free now. Free men and women have no master. And I'm sure you know that I've never felt I was the master of my slaves."

"I've never felt like a slave in your house," Amy said. "You've never treated me like a slave. What must I call you, sir?"

" 'Friend Payne.' The proper title for any Quaker is 'Friend.' Well, Amy, you have been with us a long, long time — "

"I reckoned you might have forgotten that," she said.

"Oh, no!"

Mary Payne leaned forward, smiling warmly. "Why, how could we forget? You came to us when Walter was born — "

"At the Little Bird Creek plantation, it was," Amy said reflectively, as though she peered far into the past. "Then we went to the New Garden Quaker Meeting in North Carolina and stayed four years, Temple and Dolley were born there. Temple, he was a strapping young'un, had the colic, didn't he? Yelled like fury! But Dolley, she was a mite of a thing and always good and beautiful. Dolley gets her looks from you, ma'am; her disposition, too. On a May morning in 1768 she was born, and when we went back to Little Bird Creek, she was just nine months old. Isaac was the next baby in the cradle, then Lucy. In '76 we came on to Scotchtown, and soon Anna was born, then little Mary, and now it's Johnnie — "

"Yes," Mary Payne said, "that's our flock, Amy. You've not been just their nurse; you were a second mother to them all."

"I thank you for remembering," Amy said.

John Payne was still holding the manumission paper. "You understand the value of this paper, Amy? Once you've accepted it, you're free. You can come and go as you will, anywhere, at any time. I have no further claim on you; nobody has."

She eyed the paper doubtfully. "Is that what it says?"

"Yes. Take it."

"Do you swear that it says I can go wherever I want to?"

"A Quaker never swears," he replied. "Oaths are forbidden to Quakers. But you must know that I wouldn't deceive you."

Deliberately Amy put out her hand for the paper. "Very well," she said. "I thank you, and I'll go to Philadelphia with you."

John Payne was surprised. "I see you *don't* understand — "

"Didn't you tell me that nobody has a claim on me, that I was free?"

"I did. But you can't go to Philadelphia!"

"Why not?"

"Because — because it's impossible."

"So you'll desert me? Leave me at Scotchtown to wither and die?"

"*Desert* you, Amy?"

"All this long while I've had no folks but yours," she said quietly, "no home but yours. The Negroes who worked in your fields, they'll find other fields to till, or get jobs in the villages, the towns. It's different with me. I've been a house servant, looking after children — though not in a house of my own, or my own children. You've freed me, yes — and what's to become of me now, in Virginia, where slaves are so cheap? I'm not young, and who'll employ me? Who'll shelter me, even? I don't know. I'd have to hunt and hunt — and maybe never find a shelter. But I'm not so old that I couldn't be useful to you for many years more. I'm not weak or sickly; I'd never become a burden to you. You've needed me; I think you'll need me again, in the city."

John Payne had been listening openmouthed and genuinely distressed. He had not foreseen this angle to his problem; it perplexed him. "I would have to pay you wages in Philadelphia, Amy."

"Wages? Money? I've never had money," she said. "I wouldn't know what to do with it."

"But if you worked without pay, your manumission would amount to nothing."

"You'd give me food, a bed to sleep on. I'd have the children around me like always. That's as much as I'd want."

"No," he said. "No, there's a principle at stake — "

Mary Payne spoke suddenly. "Wait, John."

"Mary, you must certainly agree with me!"

"I agree that there's a principle at stake, but we must not be hasty," she said. "I think it's a fact that Amy might have difficulty in finding employment. We've been her only family; it may seem to her that we're deserting her now. We don't wish

Amy to suffer through any act of ours, John, however righteous the act may be in itself."

"No," he said. "Oh, no."

"I believe that by economizing in other ways, we could pay her a small wage, John."

"You do?" He drummed his knuckles on the desk. "Well, I don't know. I'm in a quandary — "

"Perhaps if you prayed about it?"

"Yes," he said. "I will. I'll pray."

Mary Payne got up, beckoning to Amy and to Dolley. They went into the hall, and Mary softly closed the parlor door.

"Amy," she said, "I know what will be the answer to my husband's prayer. And somehow I'll manage the wages."

"Oh, then Amy's really going with us? I'm so glad!" Dolley exclaimed. "We do need you, Amy, and we love you very much. Mother, you're the best manager in the world, the very best."

Tears brightened Amy's fine eyes, but she winked them away. "I'll see that you never regret it, ma'am," she murmured.

3

NEW HORIZONS

Early in June the Paynes — and Amy — were ready to set out for their new home in Philadelphia.

"I thought we had sold or discarded most of our possessions, but we still seem to have mountains of trunks, bags and parcels to move," Dolley said to Temple on their last day at Scotchtown.

"Yes. And have you thought about my crocodile grin?" he asked teasingly. "Have you noticed it?"

She laughed. "Very sweet, very becoming."

"I've been down into the cellar, Dolley. I charcoaled your motto on the wall: WHAT CAN'T BE CURED MUST BE ENDURED. For the ghosts."

"I'm sure the ghosts will appreciate it," she said.

John Payne had told his wife and children that the journey would be lengthy — and it was. They traveled by stagecoach, then on a packet boat, then overland again to the Delaware River, where they embarked on a slow, unwieldy barge that chugged upstream toward their destination. But to Dolley, who had never traveled at all before, the experience was never tiresome. She felt that she was turning the pages of a book, with something different and enthralling to be glimpsed on each page. Whether jolting on dusty roads or crouched between bales of freight on a damp and sooty boat deck, she was alert and uncomplaining.

The ever-changing scenery glided by, and one hot July morning the Paynes saw the looming skyline of Philadelphia. As the barge bumped against the wooden pilings of the wharf and into its moorings, Temple cried: "There's Walter!"

Yes, there was Walter on the pier. They stood at the barge railing and gazed at him, the oldest of the Payne flock.

"How he's grown!" said his mother. "Why, Walter is a *man*."

"He does look like a man," Dolley said.

"A town fellow, by jinks," said Temple. "A clerk."

The gangplank was lowered and they trooped off the barge. Walter rushed to embrace them, his parents, Amy, his sisters and brothers. They all talked at once, and Mary Payne wept a little because it was so good that they could be together again.

"The Drinkers have invited us to dine," Walter said, when the excitement had subsided. "We'll drive to their house. I've hired two carriages for the day and after dinner I'll show you *our* house." He smiled at his mother, who was clinging to his hand. "Ladies and girls in the first carriage, ma'am; men and boys in the second, with the luggage."

In just a moment they were bundled into the carriages, whisking through streets crowded with vehicles of every description. Dolley strained to see and hear everything. Horses' hoofs pounded clop-clop on cobblestones, wheels clattered. The sidewalks seemed to stream with people. Vendors shouted their wares of fruit, vegetables, kindling, crockery and a dozen other commodities. Somewhere a whistle was blowing, a dog barking. A church bell struck ten mellow chimes and was echoed by bells from other steeples. The whole city, Dolley thought, vibrated with their pealing.

The carriage swept on, then stopped at the snow-white doorstep of a tall brick house. Here on the pavement the Drinkers were hovering expectantly.

"My dear Friend Mary," said Mrs. Drinker, as Mary Payne alighted. "What a trip you've had! Are you exhausted? Come in, come in!"

The Drinker girls, Sally and Nancy, smiled shyly at Dolley.

"Are you hungry?" they asked. "Do say yes, for we've cooked a *lovely* dinner."

The Drinkers had been born and reared in Philadelphia. They liked their city and wanted the Paynes to like it, too. At the dinner table. Mr. Drinker described it enthusiastically.

"It's one of the biggest cities in America," he said. "We have a population of thirty thousand souls, a college and a medical school, a hospital, an orphan asylum, ten newspapers, a circulating library — "

"And Benjamin Franklin," said his wife.

"And a model prison," said Sally.

"And if your house should catch fire, a volunteer fire brigade will dash to extinguish the blaze," said Nancy. "The firemen have ladders and leather buckets and caps like enormous black coal scuttles."

Mr. Drinker chuckled and said he trusted the Paynes would have no need of the prison or the fire brigade. He talked of the stirring happenings in Philadelphia in Revolutionary days. Here the Continental Congress had met to challenge the tyranny of George III of England. Here Thomas Jefferson had written the famous Declaration of Independence. In the autumn of 1777 British forces commanded by Lord Howe had captured the city. For eight months Lord Howe had made it his headquarters, and his soldiers in their smart scarlet jackets had been as thick in the streets as flies at a honey jar.

Now, of course, the war was over. General Washington was disbanding the American army and in Paris representatives of England and of the United States were negotiating a peace treaty.

"Benjamin Franklin, Philadelphia's foremost citizen, is one of these representatives," Mr. Drinker continued. "The war is over, now we have to prove that we can survive as a nation. At present we're united by the Articles of Confederation, which George Washington has said is a 'rope of sand' and will not suffice. James Madison, Alexander Hamilton and most of our great statesmen are of the opinion that a firm, strong central government must be organized. They feel it should be done soon."

This conversation, Dolley thought, was not like any she had ever heard at Scotchtown. The results of the war, the nation's future were topics of which her father had said nothing, and she was embarrassed to realize how little she knew of them. Oh, Benjamin Franklin and Alexander Hamilton were vaguely familiar names, and Mr. Madison was the man John Payne admired for his religious tolerance. Thomas Jefferson and General Washington were somewhat better known to her. In his youth, in Albemarle County, Mr. Jefferson had been a neighbor — yes, and a beau! — of her mother's. Mary Coles Payne still spoke of him at times. And General Washington? Well, the Paynes could count that peerless hero as almost a relative — for hadn't Cousin Patrick Henry married Miss Dorothea Dandridge, who was a niece of Martha Washington's, the General's wife?

Sally Drinker nudged Dolley's elbow. "Is something wrong, Dolley?"

"No, no," she said, smiling.

"You're not eating your rice pudding. Don't you relish it?"

"The pudding is delicious, Sally."

"But you look so *serious* — "

"Not serious, just ignorant," she said. "I have a great deal to learn."

In the afternoon Walter, with his mother, Amy and the youngsters drove to the house he had rented. John Payne and Temple said they wanted exercise and preferred to walk.

"Why not a walking party?" Mr. Drinker suggested. "My daughters and I will go. And would you like to walk, Dolley?"

"Yes," she said. "It's the best way to see things."

"Much the best. Six of us, to walk in double file," Mr. Drinker said. "Friend John, you and I will head our little procession."

The pavement was only a strip of cinders edging the street, spaced at intervals with wooden pumps and tall iron posts.

"I suppose you get your water supply from the pumps," Dolley said to Sally, who was her partner. "But these posts are queer. What are they for?"

"To protect pedestrians from reckless drivers," Sally answered. "The traffic can be very dangerous. You'll not think the posts so queer at night. Then the watchman hangs oil lamps on them and they look quite nice."

The houses that lined both sides of the street were high and narrow, built of brick, with shuttered windows and front doors opening directly on the pavement.

"Are the gardens in the back?" Dolley asked. "I brought

some slips of our cinnamon rosebush from Virginia."

"Gardens are rare in the city," Sally said. "We have small back yards — for drying the wash. But you'll probably find places for a rosebush or two."

"The doorsteps all gleam so!" Dolley said. "Like rows of regular white teeth."

Sally laughed. "They ought to gleam! They're scoured and chalked twice a week, winter and summer, rain or shine. It's a kind of unwritten rule in Philadelphia. Nancy and I take turns at our doorstep. If it has a single speck of dirt on it, we feel positively disgraced!"

"Dear me! I must see to it that the doorstep Walter has got for us is properly chalked."

"Your servant Amy can do it, can't she?"

"No, Amy will have her hands full, what with tending Johnnie and my youngest sisters," Dolley said. "Lucy calls Anna and Mary 'infants,' and really they are. Anna is five, and Mary not yet three. No, the doorstep will be work for me."

"You mustn't think, Dolley, that living in Philadelphia is all work and no play," Sally said earnestly. "Nancy and I go to teas and picnics — "

"You do!"

"Some Quakers aren't terribly strict. My father isn't."

"Mine is," Dolley said. "Terribly!"

They had reached a district of shops. A fashionably attired lady was emerging from a milliner's shop at the corner. Dolley's pace lagged, and she clutched Sally's sleeve.

"Heavens, what are you staring at?" Sally demanded.

"That *hat!*" Dolley breathed. "Isn't it marvelous? Those feathers and the purple ribbons? And see the lady's parasol?

Oh, imagine having a parasol! How I should love it!"

Sally giggled. "Do hasten, Dolley," she said. "If we loiter, Temple and Nancy will be treading on our heels."

"I am ever mindful of William Penn's purpose in establishing this city," John Payne was saying to Henry Drinker. "I am inspired to reflect that for a century it's been a haven for persecuted people of our faith. I am gratified to see so many citizens wearing the Quaker costume."

"Yes," said Mr. Drinker. "The Quaker costume is not a novelty here."

"You will recall, Friend Henry, what William Penn said: 'Let thy garments be plain and simple. If thou art clean and warm, thy end is accomplished; to do more is to rob the poor.' I have had my daughter Dolley memorize the quotation."

"Ah?" said Mr. Drinker. "And what does Dolley think of William Penn's words?"

"She is impressed by them. Dolley would never dispute our Quaker discipline. She is a sensible girl."

"She's a handsome girl," Mr. Drinker said. "I fear that the thoughts of my own girls may stray occasionally to frivolity. But it doesn't disturb me. My parents must have entertained the same misgivings about me when I was their age."

"About your Meeting, Friend Henry," John Payne said. "The Pine Street Monthly Meeting. I shall not feel secure or happy until I'm affiliated with it. I have letters of recommendation for myself and my family. I was the clerk of our Meeting at Cedar Creek and frequently preached the sermon there."

"You will be a valuable recruit to our Pine Street membership," said Mr. Drinker heartily. "I think you told me that you mean to buy a business in Philadelphia? I know of one that will

soon be available. A starch merchant of my acquaintance wants
to sell his trade. Starch is a luxury goods, but there's a profit to
be made in it. If you like, I can introduce you to this man. He
has his store right in his home — which is not an uncommon
arrangement in the city. By combining his store with his home,
a merchant saves on rent and other expenses."

"The arrangement would be wise for me!" John Payne
nodded. "I'm in reduced circumstances, rather pinched for
money. And, of course, a Quaker can't go into debt — not if he
wishes to remain a Quaker."

"No." Mr. Drinker paused. "It occurs to me that our discipline may be too rigid on that score. An honest man may contract debts that, because of misfortune, he cannot discharge
when due. If he is not at fault, isn't it a cruelty to humiliate him
further by publicly banishing him from the Society of Friends?"

"Not at all," John Payne said, emphatically. "Why, Friend
John, I'm surprised at you, questioning our discipline! But isn't
this Walter's rig hitched at the curb? So this is my dwelling. It
is very like yours."

"It's cut to the city pattern," Mr. Drinker said. "Three rooms
on the ground floor, three upstairs, crowned by an attic."

Cut to the city pattern. . . .

Several hours later, at an upstairs window, Dolley looked
down into the street. In the room behind her Anna and little
Mary lay asleep on a trundle bed, Lucy was delving into an
open satchel.

"Aren't you going to undress, Dolley?" Lucy asked. "Don't
you want your nightgown?"

"Yes, get it for me," Dolley said.

Lucy rummaged through the contents of the satchel. "Things

are in a horrid tangle. Oh, now I have it." She tossed the gown to Dolley. "You know, Sister, I don't mind rooming with you — if only we didn't have those infants in here! They'll probably wake us at the crack o' dawn."

"I'll be up at dawn, anyway, and off to market with Mother."

"Isn't it crazy to think of *buying* potatoes and onions and bacon, Dolley? At Scotchtown, we just *had* them." There were sounds overhead, and Lucy's eyes twinkled mischievously. "That's the boys and Amy in the attic. What a squeeze! Isaac will hate it. He and Temple will *howl*."

"They have nothing to howl about. Amy and Johnnie are in the little room under the eaves; they'll not interfere with the boys."

"At Scotchtown we'd call the little room a closet — "

"But we aren't at Scotchtown, are we?" Though Dolley's voice was brisk, she felt desperately homesick for an instant. Swallowing a lump in her throat, she said: "Come and see the street lamps, Lucy. They look nice lighted, as Sally Drinker told me they would. And there's a lady riding in a sedan chair. She has her hair powdered, like a storybook princess."

Barefoot, in her long muslin gown, Lucy padded to the window and leaned on the sill. "How many people are out! Where have they been, where are they going?"

"I don't know. Perhaps to a grand reception somewhere. Hark, somebody's scraping a fiddle. I can't quite get the tune."

"Who's *that*, Dolley?" Lucy pointed to a figure trudging below, a man in a high-collared coat, swinging a lantern.

Before Dolley could reply, the man shouted resoundingly: *"Nine of the clock and all's well!"*

"My lands!" Lucy gasped. "Who is he?"

"The watchman," Dolley said. "He'll be passing every hour of the night."

"And *shouting?* But how will we sleep?"

"Just like tops," Dolley said. "Jump into bed now, Lucy. We won't fret about anything, will we? We're in Philadelphia, and it's nine of the clock and all *is* well."

4

CITY SEASONS

It was amazing, Dolley thought, how quickly the Paynes felt at home in Philadelphia. That very summer her father became a starch merchant, taking over the downstairs front room of the house for his store, with Temple as his clerk. By autumn Isaac had enrolled as a pupil in the Friends' Academy, and Lucy started lessons at a Quaker dame's school. Amy cared for the little children and still could help with the cooking and cleaning, while Dolley's mother competently "managed" everything. Dolley herself sewed, knitted, mended, went to the market of mornings, a basket on her arm — and twice a week, rain or shine, was out with bristle brush and chalk, whitening the doorstep.

Henry Drinker introduced the Paynes to the Pine Street Meeting. It was known to the Quakers that John Payne had given up his slaves and prosperous Virginia farm because of his religion, and for this he was honored. Soon he was made an elder in Pine

Street and privileged, if the spirit prompted him, to preach on First Days.

The Meeting here, Dolley thought, was similar to the one at Cedar Creek. The men and boys, clad in dark coats without pockets or buttons, and wearing their round, broad-brimmed hats, sat at one side of the meeting house; on the long benches opposite sat the women and girls, attired in sober gray or drab, eyes downcast and hidden by their bonnets. But the Pine Street congregation was larger and the members seemed to be more sociably inclined than the Cedar Creek folk. After the prayers and preaching, they lingered to chat and mingle; and often they visited in each other's houses for tea or supper. The ladies called on Mary Coles Payne and she returned their calls. Sometimes Dolley went calling with her mother, or if her mother was the hostess, Dolley poured the tea and sliced the pound cake in the Paynes' small parlor.

The young Quakers had their own social gatherings, to which Dolley was invited. Once she went to an all-day picnic at the Drinkers' summer cottage on a nearby lake.

"Was it fun?" Lucy eagerly asked that night. "Did you dance?"

"Dance? Oh, no," Dolley said. "It was fun, though. We ate outdoors and we played charades."

"Was John Todd your escort? You know, the young man who moons at you in Meeting?"

"John Todd doesn't moon at me, Lucy!"

"He does so! He *moons*, I've seen him."

"You're a silly little goose, Lucy," Dolley said. "No, Jacob Downing escorted me. Of course, Jacob is really Sally Drinker's beau. I think they may get married next year."

"Well, I never dreamed Father would let you go," said Lucy.

"And he did grumble about it. He told Mother that such recrea- tions are unseemly, and he'd have set his foot down hard, if Walter and Temple hadn't been going also, to keep tabs on you."

Of all her new friends, Dolley was most attracted to Eliza- beth Collins, a slim, auburn-haired girl, the daughter of wealthy Quaker parents. Elizabeth was intelligent, lively and gay.

"I think you and I *see* things alike, Dolley," Elizabeth as- serted.

"I think we were meant to be boon companions," said Dolley.

On Saturdays the two girls often went for walks — "explor- ing" the city, with Elizabeth, who knew every corner of it, acting as Dolly's pilot and instructor. If the weather was fine, they might "explore" even to the fringes of town, wandering to the banks of the Schuylkill River. Shorter walks led them to the old State House to look at the Liberty Bell, or to the docks where all sorts of vessels, from fishermen's skiffs to great ocean-going ships, were anchored.

But most frequently they strolled toward the shops, as if lured there by a fascination they could not resist.

"Eliza," said Dolley one day, as they halted before a shop window in which bolts of taffeta and velvet were displayed, "dear Eliza, I must confess that I *love* beautiful clothes. Isn't it shocking?"

"Yes," Elizabeth said. "Oh, Dolly dear, I do, too!"

"I'd buy them if I could. That embroidered mantle — just the color of oranges."

"The mantle is exactly your style, Dolley. Regal! I'd have the violet polka dot and the pink silk mitts."

"Look, the peacock feather fan with ivory sticks."

"And the cerise shawl. Magnificent!"

They pressed their noses to the glass.

"Eliza, you will despise me," Dolley said, "but I love *jewelry*."

"Jewelry? Oh, that's worse!"

"Much worse. When I was a child, I had a piece of jewelry — "

"What!" cried Elizabeth.

"Yes, years and years ago, when I was seven. My Grandmother Payne gave it to me. Grandmother had a gold necklace and bracelets and some brooches with rubies in them. Or maybe not genuine rubies. Red stones."

"Your grandmother? But where on earth did she get them?"

"From my grandfather. They weren't Quakers, my Payne grandparents; they didn't know such things were sinful."

"Oh, well," breathed Elizabeth. "How — how nice."

"Grandmother kept her jewelry in a quilted satin box in her bureau drawer — I remember the box perfectly. She gave me the smallest of the brooches, pinned it on my dress. But I couldn't wear it there, or Father would have seen it — "

"Your father would have had a *spasm*, Dolley."

"Yes, so I pinned it underneath, on my petticoat yoke. It made me proud as Lucifer, just knowing it was mine. That's probably why I lost it."

"Lost it?" Elizabeth shrieked. "*Lost* — "

"It disappeared. I suppose it came unpinned and dropped off somewhere."

"But surely you searched for it, Dolley?"

"Oh, yes. I couldn't have told Mother, or any Quaker person — they'd have said I was rightly served. I told Amy. We searched every nook and cranny of the Scotchtown house, the yard, too."

"And never found it?"

"Never."

Elizabeth sighed. "Dolley, that's the saddest tale I ever heard."

As the seasons went by, they talked of Sally Drinker's engagement to Jacob Downing, how Sally and Jacob had risen in Meeting and announced their wish to marry. This formality of "passing the Meeting" would be repeated several times before the wedding could take place. No elder or public minister officiated at a Quaker wedding. The young couple had only to stand up, clasp hands, recite their pledges, then sign a certificate which afterward was signed by all those Society members who had seen the ceremony.

Dolley and Elizabeth speculated as to whether or not they themselves would ever marry.

"I think I'd rather have a Maltese cat, a poodle dog and a poll parrot than a husband," Dolley said, shaking her black curls.

"A poll parrot? You can't! They're heathen birds, symbols of evil and witchcraft, the discipline says so."

"Really? The discipline seems to bob up everywhere, doesn't it? I like parrots, their bright green plumage."

"Anyway, you'll get married, Dolley. There are half a dozen boys who'd jump at the chance. John Todd, for one. Quakers believe that girls should marry young. I've a notion my parents would like me to get engaged — and yours would be pleased if you were kinder to John Todd."

"Oh, Eliza!"

"Now don't put on that face, Dolley," Elizabeth admonished. "Everybody knows that John Todd's in love with you, and has been since the minute he first saw you, and is constantly calling at your house, and would propose to you if you just crooked a finger at him."

"John Todd is a lawyer. He comes to advise Father about the starch business, which isn't as busy as it should be these days."

"Starch!" Elizabeth said, sniffing. "John Todd means to marry you and I don't doubt he will; he'll probably persist until he does. And he would be a splendid husband for you, tall and nice looking, of a proper age and from an old Quaker family. His father, you know, is a schoolmaster at the Academy."

"The Academy where Isaac goes," Dolley said. "Yes, John Todd's father often switches Isaac's legs. Poor Isaac, he's so naughty at school! But, Eliza, if you think John Todd is such a prize, why don't you set your cap at him?"

"Oh, no, we wouldn't suit at all!" Elizabeth laughed and then was solemn. "Of course, I shall have to marry a Friend — as you will. Some girls marry out of Meeting. Like Betsy Wister and Kitty Morris, last year. Oh, what a fuss that was! Betsy and Kitty had fallen in love with men who weren't Quakers, and when the Society objected, they just ran off."

"They *eloped?*"

"Yes, and were married by a non-Quaker preacher. And when the Society banished them, they said they didn't care!"

"Perhaps they didn't, Eliza. Their hearts had made the choice, and love is no respecter of persons."

"But to be disowned by the Society! I shudder at the thought."

"Well, you needn't think of it," Dolley said. "It'll never be your fate. Or mine, either, because I shall never marry."

"Bosh, you will so!" Elizabeth said. "You'll be John Todd's wife. I feel it in my bones."

As Dolley had said to Elizabeth Collins, the starch business was not quite as busy as it should be; and when the Paynes had lived for a year in the city, they moved to a smaller house. A year later they moved again, to a house that was still smaller and in a less desirable neighborhood. Dolley told herself that these changes were troublesome, but not alarming. Her father's business was just a little slow in getting started. It surely would pick up as time went on.

Also she had read in the newspapers that trade was dull everywhere at present, and money scarce, because of the recent war. Any war, in any country, is always followed by a period of readjustment, the newspapers explained. Americans were uncertain about their future government. New laws must be formulated to bind the various states into a nation and to give the people confidence. And this would soon be done. In fact, a Constitutional Convention was even now being planned. It would be held right here in Philadelphia, with all the states sending their most capable leaders as delegates.

"Everybody's economizing," Dolley said to Temple. "The people who used to buy starch are making it now. When the statesmen get our government straightened out and in running order, Father will have more customers."

Temple raised his eyebrows dubiously. "I think Father never realized how expensive it would be to transplant his big family from the farm to the city. I'm afraid he hasn't the knack for trade. Well, I haven't it, either. I could work like fury at this clerk's job, work and *grin* forever, until I got old and stooped, with a beard clear down to my knees — and always as poor as a church mouse. I'm afraid we're farmers, Father and I, and nothing else. And Isaac, too. You can't fit square pegs into round holes, Dolley."

"Oh, I wish you wouldn't say such things!" she said. "I don't believe you!"

But she could not quite forget Temple's comment. Her father

was nervous and irritable. She knew that at night he sat for hours staring at his ledgers, which showed so many blank pages. Returning from market in the mornings, or from a Saturday stroll with Elizabeth, she would see him standing in the doorway of his neat and empty store, as if waiting for the customers who did not come. At such times, her heart ached for him and she wondered whether Temple had been entirely mistaken. Was her father really a square peg that could never be fitted into a round hole? And Temple and Isaac, too?

Then Walter abruptly went to England, to live in London, where he had been offered a position. Walter was discouraged by business conditions in Philadelphia; it was only natural that he should want the higher salary he could earn abroad. But somehow his departure was disconcerting to Dolley. She felt that she must try hard to make the atmosphere at home seem normal and serene.

In this she was helped by John Todd, the young lawyer. John Todd was not only in love with Dolley, he was a devoted friend to all the Paynes. Whenever he came to the house (and that was increasingly often!) he was attentive and agreeable to them all. Dolley knew that her parents looked with favor on John Todd and hoped that she would marry him.

"It would be *very* nice to have John Todd in our family, Sister," Lucy said.

Dolley smiled and thought: Well, perhaps. After a while. Next spring, next fall. There's no hurry.

The convention to devise a constitution, or body of laws, for the new United States assembled in Philadelphia in May, 1787. Every state except Rhode Island and Vermont had appointed delegates, men selected for their ability and distinction.

The people of Philadelphia were excited at the prospect of having so many famous Americans in their midst, and for several days before the convention opened, they swarmed in the streets to watch the coming of the delegates. Benjamin Franklin, who headed the Pennsylvania delegation, was beloved by all his fellow citizens; they hailed him with fervor. But there was no lack of applause for the great men from other states. The young and handsome Alexander Hamilton of New York was cheered. James Madison was pointed out: Madison looked like a serious-faced, rather undersized college student, said the crowd, and yet he was reputed to have the best education and brains of all the Virginians! Of course, the noisiest greeting was for General Washington, who drove up to the Indian Queen Hotel in coach-and-four, dressed like a fashion plate in powdered wig, black velvet coat and breeches, and yellow kid gloves.

Loud and long rang the cheers for the General: "Hurrah, hurrah, hur-*ray!*"

Dolley and John Todd were in the jostling throng that saw Washington step down from his carriage, doff his cocked hat and bow to the multitude. John had said that the convention was an important historical event. The sessions would be held in the State House.

"Secret sessions, in the very chamber where eleven years ago the Declaration of Independence was signed," he said.

"What will they do, John, in their secret sessions?" Dolley asked.

He laughed. "Argue and debate, mostly. They're not all of one mind about the laws to be made. They'll have lots of questions to thresh over. A central government is needed — but what will it be? Are the common people to have as much power as the rich and aristocratic? Some of the delegates are from small states and some from large. Are the little states to have equal representation in Congress with the big ones? And what of the thousands upon thousands of slaves in the South? In accounting the inhabitants of southern states, are the slaves to be classified as persons? And what of taxes, tariffs, foreign relations? General Washington will probably be unanimously elected to preside over the convention, because of his great popularity — and then, I think, the wrangling will begin."

"But finally the convention will produce a constitution, John?"

"It will produce something — a document to be submitted to the state legislatures," he said. "When — and if — nine states ratify the laws drafted by the delegates, the document will become our Constitution. If, however, the American people don't like what the delegates have done, and won't ratify it through their legislatures, all the labor of the convention will have been in vain."

The delegates were in session all that summer and gradually they settled the questions harassing them, a Constitution was hammered into shape. In September they adjourned. In October and until April of the following year, the newspapers printed a series of essays which explained the Constitution and urged the states to ratify it, so that a new government could be organized as speedily as possible. The essays were signed with the name "Publius," and were published as a book, entitled the *Federalist Papers*.

One evening when John Todd came to the Paynes' house he brought with him a copy of the *Federalist Papers*.

"I thought your father might like to read the 'Publius' essays, Dolley," he said.

She thanked him. John's kindness to her family was a source of comfort now, for things were going very badly indeed with the Paynes. The starch business was so slow as to have stopped almost entirely. Her father was ever more irritable and dour. Dolley had a feeling of uneasiness, as if some crisis approached. She believed that her mother felt it, too — and perhaps Amy and Temple as well.

She took the book from John and looked at it. "I wonder who 'Publius' is. I suppose that's a pen name."

"Yes," John said. "Madison and Hamilton wrote the essays, with John Jay of New York contributing a few to the series. You haven't read them?"

"Oh, yes." She smiled. "I don't know that I quite understood them, but it was good to have something other than *starch* to think about."

"The essays are having an effect," John said. "Six states have ratified, it may not be long before three more fall in line. Of course, Alexander Hamilton is influential, and now many people are saying that James Madison is a great lawyer. The 'great little Madison' — so he's called — the 'Father of the Constitution.' "

"I wish I might have seen Mr. Madison the day we went to the Indian Queen." Dolley put the book on the table. "I've always been rather curious about him."

"Let's forget government matters for the moment, let's not be earnest," John said. "Do you know it's spring again, a beautiful night, with stars galore? Come outdoors, Dolley."

They sat on a rustic bench in the small patch of garden behind the house. The stars were bright, a warm breeze blew softly.

"When are you going to marry me, Dolley?" John asked. "I'm proposing to you for what must be the twentieth time."

She was silent. Seated there beside her, John Todd looked solid and strong. She was fond of him, flattered by his steadfast devotion, perhaps she loved him. But marriage was such a *lasting* thing!

"Your parents would be glad of the match, they've told me so," he said. "My parents wish for it — and the Pine Street Meeting would think it very suitable. I could make you happy, Dolley. My law practice is growing rapidly. I know of a good house we could rent, and in a little while we could buy or build a better one." He paused. "Well, my dear?"

She roused herself and said: "I don't want to marry anybody yet, John."

"You're twenty — "

"Almost an old maid! Oh, I'm sure I *should* want to get married. But — no, you must look elsewhere for a wife."

"That I'll never do," he said. "Never! I'll just keep on asking you until you answer yes! Dolley, I could help you, your father — "

"I know that we need help," she murmured. "But still I — I can't decide."

He took her hand and kissed it. "I really think that you know you're going to marry me. I think you're only waiting for something to happen that will seem to decide it for you. And I think the something will happen!"

"John, are you a prophet?"

"I may be," he said. "We shall see, Dolley."

5

SOME DECISIONS

By July 4, 1788, more than the required number of state legislatures had ratified the Constitution, and the new government was launched. In January, 1789, George Washington was elected without a dissenting vote as the first President of the United States, and John Adams of Massachusetts became the first Vice-President. Like many other American cities, Philadelphia celebrated these events with parades of colorful floats, band music and marching people. But to the Payne family they seemed to have little meaning. Dolley herself scarcely heeded them at all, for now she was absorbed in the sad bewilderment prevailing at home.

John Payne's business had failed now utterly. He was ruined financially, penniless. One dark day he shuttered the windows of his store, put his round Quaker hat on his head and strode out of the house. He was going to consult with the elders in Pine Street, he said. He had something to tell the elders.

Dolley would never forget the results of that consultation. At evening he came staggering into the kitchen where Dolley and her mother were preparing the supper. He lurched into a chair and hid his face in his hands. In a quivering voice, he muttered that he had been banished from the Society of Friends.

"Banished?" cried Mary Payne. "Why? *Why?*"

He said that in an attempt to save his business he had borrowed from moneylenders, supposing that he could repay the debts.

"But I couldn't," he said. "The debts are overdue, I have nothing. My creditors are hounding me. So I've made my plight known to the Pine Street Meeting — and they have acted."

Dolley saw that he was weeping. Suddenly he seemed to her like a child who must be pitied and consoled, and she knelt beside him. "Oh, Father, the Society is wrong — "

He pushed her away. "The Society is not wrong," he said coldly. "The Society cannot be wrong. The Society has rules; members must abide by them or bear the consequences."

"But to treat you so harshly — "

"I did not abide by the rules, Dolley. Therefore, *I* am wrong. The Society is not to be criticized, I will not have it!"

He struggled to his feet and went into his bedroom and closed the door behind him. He lay down on his bed. When his wife and daughter rapped on the door, he shouted hoarsely that he wanted to be alone with his misery.

The night passed, the next day, a week, a month. He would not get up or speak to anyone, he barely tasted the food that was brought to him. Stretched on his bed, he stared mutely at the ceiling, his eyes clouded, his mouth tight lipped.

Mary Payne was terribly worried. She had the doctor in, and

afterward she beckoned Dolley and Temple into the front room that had been the starch store.

"The doctor says your father's illness is more mental than physical," she told them. "There's no medicine to be prescribed, not much we can do for him. He can get well only if he wishes to, and this may be difficult for him because in losing his identity as a Quaker, he has lost the thing he valued most in life."

Mary sighed; impulsively Dolley ran to kiss her. Temple was fingering the ledgers on John Payne's desk, flicking through the blank pages, frowning at them. He turned and went to the window, unlatched the shutters and looked out.

"We must think of what we can do for ourselves," Mary said, rubbing her forehead. "For the younger children and Amy. How are we to live?"

"I know what I can do," Temple said. "Go back to Virginia. I'm not a clerk now; my job evaporated with Father's trade. I'll go back and get work as a farm hand. Yes, and take Isaac with me. Isaac is eighteen, forever in one scrape or another at the Academy and being flogged for it. A plantation is the place for Isaac and me, and we'll find one to hire us. We'll send you our earnings, Mother. It may be small pickings, but we'll send it."

Dolley was fearful that her mother would be distressed by Temple's idea. Instead, Mary nodded slowly and said: "There's still that land in western Virginia — "

"What!" Temple whirled from the window.

"A few acres," Mary said. "Hilly, uncultivated. Your father never sold it; nobody ever wanted to buy it."

"Land! Isaac and I will raise tobacco, Mother!"

"You mightn't be able to raise a single crop of anything."

"You'll see!" Temple was smiling. "I never guessed we owned an *inch* of land anywhere! We'll go soon — and you mustn't fret about Isaac, ma'am. I'll watch out for him."

"I'm sure you will," Mary said.

"Isaac isn't a bad boy; he's just a bit rebellious and hot tempered."

"Yes. I'll miss you both, Temple."

"But if you know we're together — "

Mary nodded again. "Then I'll be content."

Temple talked for a moment of his plans. He seemed almost jubilant. Dolley listened, but she saw that her mother's glance had wandered. Mary was looking around the room, as if to measure it from wall to wall, and abruptly she said: "This could be made into a dining room — for boarders."

"Boarders?" Dolley echoed. "What do you mean, Mother?"

"I've been thinking of advertising for them," Mary said. "It's not something that has just crossed my mind. We've had a money shortage for months, haven't we? And now it's acute. Well, the Philadelphia inns and taverns can't accommodate one third of the people who come to the city. The Indian Queen is a modern hotel, but I've heard that last year the convention delegates were disgruntled at the meals served them. I'm a good cook, all southern women know how to cook — "

Temple interrupted. "You're a southern *lady,* ma'am."

She smiled. "And you think I should be less a lady with boarders at my dining table?"

"No, no," he said. "Of course not! But the hard work — "

"I don't fear that. Amy and Lucy would help me."

"*I'd* help you, Mother," Dolley said.

Mary hesitated. "Perhaps this is the time for you to marry John Todd, my daughter. He loves you, and you love him — don't you?"

Dolley flushed. "I — I'm very fond of John."

"I see no earthly reason why you shouldn't marry him, and there are many reasons for it. With your father so sick, Walter in England, Temple and Isaac going back to Virginia, and our Johnnie such a little fellow, not eight years old, John Todd would be a tower of strength to us. A man in the family!" Mary's smile was wistful. "I wouldn't say it, Dolley, if I didn't know that you truly love him."

Dolley's cheeks were hot. Was this the something John had prophesied? It did seem so. Why not marry him? The decision was being made for her, this was the time for it. And her feeling for him was more than fondness — it was love. She said to herself that when John came tonight, she would tell him!

They were married January 7, 1790, in the Pine Street Meeting House, for the Friends had never held Mary Payne or her children responsible for John Payne's misfortunes, and the Todds were highly esteemed among Philadelphia Quakers. Dolley wore her plain gray gown and white neckerchief. The Friends said that she looked modest and demure — a proper Quaker bride.

"And John is *beaming*," Elizabeth Collins whispered to Dolley. "His long perseverance has been at last rewarded. Oh, this is *Fate!*"

On three previous First Days, they had stood up before the congregation. Now, again they rose and, hand in hand, said their simple vows.

John spoke first: "I, John Todd, do take thee, Dolley Payne, to be my wedded wife, and promise with divine assistance to be unto thee a loving and faithful husband until death shall separate us."

Then Dolley responded, her blue eyes serenely shining, her voice calm: "I, Dolley Payne, do take thee, John Todd, to be my wedded husband, and promise with divine assistance to be unto thee a loving and faithful wife until death shall separate us."

6

QUAKER WIFE

John Todd's law practice was growing by leaps and bounds.
After a year of married life in a rented cottage, he bought a
large new house, which Dolley furnished nicely with mahogany
and pine, carpets, mirrors and those stoves called Franklin
stoves that Philadelphia's Ben Franklin had recently invented.
The new house had a stable attached; John purchased a horse
and carriage so that Dolley could drive out to do her marketing.

"John, you're the most thoughtful of husbands," she said.

He laughed. "It would be nearer the mark to say I'm the
luckiest. I've commissioned the artist, Charles Peale, to paint
your portrait, Dolley."

"Charles Peale? Oh, that *is* an extravagance."

"No," John said. "The portrait is for the child we're expecting — our son."

The portrait, a miniature painted on ivory, was an accurate
likeness of Dolley at twenty-two. And, as if John veritably had

the power to prophecy, the child, born in February of 1792, was a son.

They named the baby John Payne Todd, for Dolley's father. "We'll call him Payne," she said. "I hope Father will be pleased to have a grandson named for him."

But John Payne gave no indication of pleasure, or of interest in little Payne. He was an invalid now, a recluse, weak, petulant and bedridden.

"Father's illness is beyond my comprehension," Dolley said one day when she had driven over with the baby to her mother's house. "He had a bitter disappointment, but I had thought of him as a brave man, not one who would collapse under it."

"Human beings aren't all alike," Mary said, "nor do they react alike to adversity. We must not judge your father."

"I've seen your reaction to adversity, Mother. You don't collapse, you strike back."

"That's my nature, Dolley. And yours, I think, is the same."

"Well, have women more courage than men?"

"We have a different kind of courage, perhaps. And we're more accustomed to dealing with disappointments." Mary looked down at the baby nestled into his padded and beribboned basket. She lifted Payne into her lap and rocked him and crooned to him. "What a beautiful child he is, Dolley. Brown eyes, thick brown hair — he reminds me of Lucy when she was an infant. You know that Lucy adores Payne? She wishes she had nothing to do but play with him. It seems to me that she's at your house most of the time."

"Lucy is a dear," Dolley said. "We're always glad to have her there."

With the baby dozing in her arms, Mary talked of her experiment at keeping boarders. It was turning out to be a success, she said. Now that the Congress met in Philadelphia, the city was more crowded than ever. She had not advertised her southern cooking. Word of it had somehow got about, she soon had her table full. One of her guests was Senator Aaron Burr of New York, an urbane gentleman so appreciative of her good food that he frequently brought other government officials to sample it.

"Then I have to scramble around, setting up extra chairs, while Amy bakes extra batches of spoon bread and waffles," she said, smiling.

Dolley sighed. "I'm afraid it's all too much for you, Mother."

"Oh, not at all."

"I feel that I should be here, contending with Senator Aaron Burr, setting up those chairs for the hungry Congressmen."

"No, no! I wouldn't have you here. I rejoice that you finally came to your senses and married John Todd. It's what I wanted you to do. Never think you aren't helping me, Dolley! It's the greatest blessing to me to know that I have you to rely on. You're a dutiful daughter, and good, generous John is the best of sons-in-law. I rejoice to see you so happy. You *are* happy, aren't you?"

"I'm very happy," Dolley said.

One evening in the early summer Lucy came to spend the night at the Todds' house. With supper over and the dishes washed, the two sisters sat in the parlor, Lucy on the floor, amusing little Payne who lay kicking his heels on a fleecy pink blanket; Dolley in a Windsor chair, her knitting in her hands. John had gone out to interview a client. The windows were open, the curtains looped back; the red-and-gold glow of a sinking sun suffused the clean, orderly room.

Lucy tapped the baby's chin and he chuckled. "Oh, you cunning rascal," she said. "What a jolly laugh he has, Dolley. Like a fat old man."

"You're spoiling him," Dolley said. "He won't be satisfied now unless his chin is tapped."

"He is spoiled, you began to spoil him the day he was born," Lucy said frankly. "I think any child of yours would be coddled and pampered. You'd love it so much, and want it to have all the good things in the world — and none of the bad."

"Would I?" Dolley paused, considering. "Yes, I suppose that, if it was possible, I'd take on my own shoulders any bad things that may come to Payne."

"It seems, doesn't it, that everybody has both good *and* bad?"

"Yes, and some people have more bad than good, too big a load of toil and trouble. Mother is one of them."

Lucy got up rather quickly from the floor. She walked to the mantel and looked at a pair of crystal vases on the shelf. "These are pretty vases," she said. "You have a pretty parlor."

"Perhaps it's too pretty," Dolley said, "for the home of Quakers. Perhaps I'm too fond of ornaments and pretty knickknacks."

"Oh, Quakers!" Lucy exclaimed. "I wish we weren't Quakers!"

Dolley was surprised at the resentment in Lucy's voice. "Why, what a thing to say! What do you mean?"

"I mean — " Lucy hesitated. "Dolley, if John Todd hadn't been a Quaker, would you have married him anyway?"

"But he was!" Now Dolley hesitated, a disquieting notion flashing into her mind. She put aside her knitting. "Surely you're not thinking of getting married, Lucy. You're so young — "

"I'm sixteen," Lucy said. "That's not so young."

"Sixteen? I hadn't realized it! And — you think that you've fallen in love with someone?"

"Oh, I don't know." Lucy fidgeted and frowned. "I don't know what love is. But — well, there *is* someone I *like* very much. A boy I got to know last winter when the river was frozen over. I went skating — and I ran into him. We collided with a crash and a bang, and I sprawled on the ice, and he picked me up and apologized. We talked. He's from Virginia, studying here at Philadelphia College and almost ready to be graduated. And afterward, when I went skating again, he was always there."

"What is his name?" Dolley asked.

"George. He's awfully kind and courteous."

"George what?"

"Washington," Lucy said. "George Steptoe Washington."

Dolley's feeling of surprise increased. "Is he a relative of the President's?"

"Yes, George is an orphan, and President Washington is his uncle and guardian. That's why George is at the city college, to be near his Uncle George."

Dolley knew that because Philadelphia was temporarily the capital of the United States, President Washington had moved his family here from Mount Vernon, his plantation on the Potomac. But she had not known of this nephew and ward of the President's. Now she was abruptly aware that her sister Lucy was no longer a child. On the contrary, Lucy was a fresh-complexioned, graceful girl, almost a young woman — and one whom any young man might notice.

"How old is George Steptoe Washington?" Dolley asked.

"He's seventeen."

"Oh, then *he* certainly isn't thinking of marriage, and won't be thinking of it for some years."

"I suppose not," Lucy said.

"The Washingtons are not Quakers — "

"No." Lucy looked at Dolley, then looked away. "May I carry the baby upstairs to his cradle? He's sleepy."

"Of course, you may. Lucy, have you told Mother about George?"

"No, and you mustn't tell her," Lucy said. "Or John, or any-one. It's of no importance whatever."

"I won't tell," Dolley said. "Mother has enough worries as it is. And though John isn't strait laced, he would think you'd been very forward and foolish to talk with a boy you ran across skating on the river — "

"Ran *into*," Lucy said. "Oh, Dolley, I had to talk to him! He picked me up and said how sorry he was. I couldn't just *gawk* at him, as if I were deaf and dumb, could I? Maybe I need not have talked to him the other times — but, well, I did. But it's all just much ado about nothing. I may never see him again, I don't go around *seeking* him, you know."

"If you should see him, merely by chance, you won't forget that he is not a Quaker?"

"Oh, no," Lucy said, rather grimly. "I'm not likely to forget that!"

An hour later John came in and found Dolley alone in the parlor.

"Where is Lucy?" John asked. "Isn't she staying the night?"

"She took the baby upstairs and then must have gone to bed herself," Dolley replied.

John pulled a chair close and sat down. "I stopped to see

your father on my way home. He will last only a few days, Dolley. I'll write to Walter in England, and to Temple and Isaac, but even though they came at once, I fear they wouldn't be in time."

"Oh, poor Father," she murmured. "To have sacrificed so much — and in vain."

"My dear, it was not in vain," John said. "He was guided by the Inner Light and obedient to it. For a man of his deep faith, nothing could be more worth while."

"But that it should end like this, affecting the lives of others, Mother's life — "

"The slightest deed of any person affects the lives of others, Dolley. You cannot believe that your mother would have opposed his freeing those enslaved Negroes, even had she known this would be the end of it?"

"No," Dolley said. "I'm sure of that."

John Payne's death was mourned by his wife and children and a meager group of friends. The Drinkers, Elizabeth Collins and John Todd's parents went to the funeral services, but he had been shut off from the world for so long that most of the people of the Pine Street Meeting had forgotten his existence and his death was like the passing of a shadow.

Then, very suddenly, Amy died.

As the Paynes wept for Amy, it was discovered that she had left a will, bequeathing five hundred dollars to Mary Payne.

"But how could she?" Dolley said. "How could Amy have had *anything* to bequeath?"

"It was the wages we paid her," Mary said tearfully. "She had hoarded every cent of her wages all these years. Oh, Dolley, I think of the day in the old house at Scotchtown, her reluctance to take the manumission paper from your father. He was so perplexed!"

"Until you spoke for her to come with us, Mother."

"Yes, I did."

"I remember Amy's saying that she wouldn't know what to do with money, and that you'd never regret speaking for her."

"But I didn't want to be compensated for it! I don't think I can accept this bequest — "

"You must, Mother," Dolley said. "And more for Amy's sake than your own. The thing I remember so well is that Amy never felt like a slave in our family. We were her people, she loved us all, and you best of all. You must let her help you in this way. It proves, doesn't it, that she was really free?"

7

TROUBLED TIMES

The next spring Lucy married George Steptoe Washington. The wedding was performed by a minister of the Episcopal Church, to which the youthful bridegroom belonged — but Lucy insisted that it was not an elopement!

"The word 'elope' has a sly and tricky sound," Lucy said, when she told Dolley the astonishing news. "I didn't deceive Mother, she knew all about it. George has finished his schooling. He's going back to take charge of Harewood, the plantation he inherited from his father. Of course, he wanted me to go with him. He said he couldn't live without me! I begged Mother to consent to our marriage; on my knees I begged her. But she said never, *never*. So what were we to do?"

"What was Mother's objection to George?" Dolley asked.

"Only that he's not a Quaker. No other objection would be possible, for George is perfect, Dolley. He really is!" Lucy turned the gold ring on her finger. "Oh, we're sorry to displease

Mother; we pray that she'll forgive us. If she had said that she couldn't consent because we're so young, we might have waited a bit. But however long we waited, George still wouldn't have been a Quaker. Waiting wouldn't have changed that."

"No, I suppose not. What do the Washingtons think about the marriage?"

Lucy smiled. "We did have their consent. George had talked with his uncle. You may not believe it, but President Washington and his wife seem to like me very well."

"I believe you," Dolley said, and added: "You know, don't you, that you'll be banished from the Society?"

"Yes, I know."

"A committee in Pine Street is probably drawing up the resolution now. It will be signed by the entire membership."

"Will you and John sign?"

"I think John will say that we must." Dolley's voice faltered. "How I detest it, Lucy! Who am I, to condemn you? If it weren't for John, I should refuse."

"Oh, I understand," Lucy said sturdily. "I'll not be angry with you."

"I couldn't bear it if you were!"

"You may be sure I won't, Sister. It's funny, though, the ideas people have of what's right and what's wrong. I think it's right for me to marry George — I know it is! And some of the Society's rules seem wrong to me. I think the Friends were horrid and unfair to banish Father."

"He didn't feel that they were, Lucy."

"If they hadn't read him out of Meeting, he would be alive today."

"No," Dolley said. "Now you're being unfair. That's passing a judgment, a thing that Mother says we must not do. Instead of blaming the Quaker faith for Father's trials and tribulations, we must remember how it has always sustained and solaced Mother. It's a splendid faith."

Lucy put on her bonnet, for she was traveling immediately to Harewood with George. "Oh, well," she said, and her eyes were misty. "I hope above everything else that Mother will forgive me. Good-by, Dolley. Kiss little Payne for me. You *will* come to see me sometime?"

"Of course, I will," Dolley answered. "You'll never be banished from my love, you know."

The summer was excessively, swelteringly hot in Philadelphia.

One humid day when the sun glared like a disc of brass in the sky, a second son was born to the Todds, and named William Temple, for Dolley's brother. This baby was frailer than little Payne had been at birth, and Dolley was slow to regain her strength. Her mother, who was caring for them both, said that she would stay on through the month, her boarders could shift for themselves.

"It's a slack season," Mary Payne said. "Most of the boarders have fled from the heat into the country — or have been frightened off by reports of the yellow fever."

The yellow fever? . . .

Dr. Benjamin Rush, Philadelphia's eminent physician, recorded in his diary that on August 5, 1793, a patient of his had died of a strange and "malignant" ailment. Two weeks later, he recorded that the ailment was spreading. It seemed, he said, "to mock the power of medicine." In most cases it was fatal.

How had it started? In July a boatload of immigrants from Santo Domingo had disembarked at the Philadelphia docks: had these newcomers brought with them the germs of some dread tropical disease? Or were the germs carried by the mosquitoes that swarmed up in clouds from the river bottoms these damp and sultry nights? There had never been such big and savage mosquitoes!

Dr. Rush was a scientist; he would have liked to trace the fever to its source and analyze the cause — but he was too busy, hurrying from patient to patient, easing them as best he could, though knowing that the tide of infection was not to be stemmed. All the doctors and surgeons in the city were frantically fighting the fever, and some of them caught it and died themselves. Dr. Rush kept on his feet and called for volunteers to nurse the sick and bury the dead.

As more and more victims were claimed, panic swept Philadelphia. This was an epidemic as terrible as the historic London Plague of 1665, and most people had but one thought: to get away from it! By day and by night the streets were choked with their trundling wagons and carts, the houses they left behind them were darkened, desolate. Those citizens who remained soaked their clothing with vinegar water and burned smudge fires, believing that the fumes might give them immunity. A reek of vinegar mingled with the ascending pall of smoke to fill the air.

But as in every time of calamity, there were people who were steadfast and fearless, and now the Quakers demonstrated the teachings of their splendid faith. They were charitable, donating large sums to the relief funds that newspapers collected. They responded, in groups and as individuals, to the cry for volunteers and never shrank from danger. Their deeds of heroism were too numerous to be reckoned.

Dr. Rush's diary noted that among the most tireless of the Quaker workers was John Todd. . . .

At the very onset of the epidemic John took his family to Gray's Ferry, a village on the Schuylkill River. Mary Payne and her girls, Anna and Mary, and eleven-year-old Johnnie Payne, went with them. The fever had not invaded Gray's Ferry; the place was jammed with refugees, but John got lodgings for them.

"You'll be safe here, Dolley," he said.

She clung to him. He was going back to the city, to his parents, who were old and feeble and could not be moved from their home. "Oh, John!" she said, "If only you were as safe! When will I see you again?"

"As soon as the pestilence abates," he said.

"Not before?"

"That may be very soon," he said.

In September Dolley had messages from him. The pestilence had not yet abated. Doctors estimated that four thousand people had died of it. John's parents were dead; he had attended to their burial.

In October he wrote more cheerfully. The weather was cooler, Dr. Rush said that new cases were fewer, the epidemic was on the wane.

"I'll come to Gray's Ferry, October 24," John wrote.

Dolley counted the days. He arrived at noon on the 24th. Mary Payne opened the door to him and he stumbled in, sweating, gasping for breath.

"John, you have the fever!" Mary cried.

"Where is Dolley?" he said. "I must see Dolley."

"No, John. No! — "

But Dolley had heard him and was in the room, clasping him in her arms.

"I was stricken on the way to you," he muttered.

They got him into bed; he closed his eyes, groaning in anguish.

That night Dr. Benjamin Rush reported in his diary: "John Todd, the lawyer, died this afternoon."

The next day Dolley and the baby Temple were ill with the fever. Mary Payne nursed them tenderly, and by late November Dolley had recovered sufficiently to be up and dressed. But the baby's fragile thread of life had snapped; the baby was dead.

December's icy cold nipped the contagion, refugees straggled back to the city. By Christmastime Dolley was at home — in a house that seemed intolerably bleak and lonely. On the last day of the year Lucy found her there.

"George sent me," Lucy said. "George wants you to come and live with us, Dolley. You and Payne, Mother, Johnnie, Anna, Mary — all of you. Harewood is an immense house, and George is a rich man. I never thought of that when we were skating and laughing and getting acquainted. I never would have dreamed it. But he is rich —and he's *good*, the soul of hospitality."

Dolley smiled wanly. "He must be!"

"George says why should Mother be so hard pressed while we have so much? He says she must make her home with us and never do another lick of work. And you, too. He says I'm to bring you to Harewood — everybody, bag and baggage, where he'll provide for you." Lucy paused. "Dolley, do you think Mother has forgiven me?"

"She may always wish you hadn't married out of Meeting," Dolley said, "but she loves you."

"She'll love George when she knows him. I haven't seen her yet. How is she? How does she look?"

"Weary — and thin."

"Well, consider what she's been through! And you, Dolley, you're thin as a rail, your suffering shows in your face. Of course, the miracle is that you've survived. Do come to Harewood! And coax Mother to come!"

Dolley thought for a moment. "I believe Mother can be persuaded; I'll talk to her. As for me, I thank you and George with all my heart, but I feel that I must live here."

"Oh, no, Sister!"

"Yes, Lucy. You may wonder that I should have the desire to live at all, anywhere. I wonder at myself! But I have. Somehow I can't admit that I'm beaten, defeated. I've still got Payne — and the whole responsibility for him, which I must not shirk. I feel that our place, Payne's and mine, is here in our own home."

"I wish you didn't feel so," Lucy said, "but neither George nor I would presume to dictate to you. Well, if you stay in Philadelphia, you should have somebody with you, an older person than Payne. What about Anna? She's fourteen now and quite a sensible girl."

"You think Anna would want to stay with me?"

"I'm positive of it. Ask her."

"Yes," Dolley said. "I will. I'll ask Anna."

Always, Dolley thought, after any disaster, somebody has to gather up and sort out the wreckage, and see what can be done with it!

"Anna," she said, "we must put this house in order — and ourselves also."

Anna nodded. Tall, dark haired and vivacious, she had been told that she looked like Dolley, and her wish was to be like her older sister in everything. She imitated Dolley's gestures and tone of voice, and combed her curls in the same soft waves on cheeks and forehead.

"But perhaps it will be dreary for you here, Anna?"

"Oh, no, I'd rather be here than at Harewood!"

"You would, honestly? Well, we must take each day as it comes," Dolley said, "and make the most of it."

Valiantly then, in the new year, with Anna's help she set about to make a satisfactory daily routine from the remnants of the past. Together they cleaned Dolley's pretty rooms; they sewed, knitted, spun flax into yarn, played with little Payne and went regularly to the Quaker Meeting in Pine Street. They were never idle, and whatever task or mild recreation Dolley suggested, Anna was ready for it.

Dolley's friends said that as a widow she seemed to be more beautiful than ever before. Elizabeth Collins teased her about it.

"Gentlemen station themselves where they can see you walking by to Meeting or to market," she said.

"Eliza, how silly!"

"No, it's a fact. They stare at you. Really, you should hide your face."

Elizabeth was engaged now to Richard Bland Lee, a young Congressman from Virginia. Mr. Lee was not a Quaker and this, she told Dolley, was a complication, though her parents were being as docile as lambs.

"I know what happened to your sister Lucy," she said. "The Society expelled her, and it will expel me. I shall be another outcast, Dolley. But, as you once remarked, love is no respecter of persons."

Dolley smiled. "I remember that you shuddered then at the mere thought of being an outcast, Eliza."

"That was before Richard crossed my path."

"So many of the younger Quakers seem to be marrying out of Meeting."

"Yes, surely the Society will have to relax its rules!"

Elizabeth and her Mr. Lee, calling on Dolley, sometimes found Senator Aaron Burr there, at the fireside. Senator Burr was handsome, brilliant, prominent in government affairs. His manners were elaborately gallant.

"But he has the reputation of a flirt, Dolley," Elizabeth warned. "I don't just fancy his friendship with you. I fear it may be thought the Senator is having a flirtation with the beautiful Widow Todd."

Dolley protested. There was no tinge of romance in her friendship with the Senator. She had known him first as a boarder in her mother's house; he had been very kind to the Paynes when her father died.

"He talks to me about his daughter Theodosia," she said. "Theodosia is the apple of his eye. He had advanced theories on the education of children. He's training his daughter by these theories, and he advises me about Payne's training. I must admit, Eliza, that some of Mr. Burr's ideas do interest me. For instance, he believes that women have as much brains as men, and should be given as much education."

Elizabeth laughed. "Well, isn't that true? Don't you think so?"

"Yes. But for a man to think it — "

"My Richard does," said Elizabeth complacently.

Often in Dolley's parlor Richard Lee and Senator Burr discussed politics. It was a period when political parties were forming around certain leaders. George Washington had been re-elected to the Presidency without opposition, but the differing views expressed by delegates to the Constitutional Convention in 1787 had sharpened, and now citizens of the United States were divided as to the actual meaning of the Constitution, how it must be interpreted and enforced.

Alexander Hamilton, the Secretary of the Treasury in President Washington's cabinet, favored a national government which would be firmly held in the grasp of a comparatively small group, or class, an aristocracy of wealth and breeding. Most men, Hamilton said, are not good and wise, but are vicious, not to be trusted. And the ordinary man, even though he might be well intentioned, is too stupid to govern himself or to participate in the government of others.

"The voice of the people," said Hamilton, "is not the voice of God."

Statesmen who shared Hamilton's opinions were known as Federalists. With them as their leader, they had founded the Federalist party.

Aligned against Hamilton and the Federalists was the Republican party, headed by Thomas Jefferson. Far from despising the common people, Jefferson believed in them, and in their ability to govern themselves. It was necessary, Jefferson said, to have a strong national government — but this should never encroach upon the private rights of citizens or the rights of the various states that composed the Union.

"Equal opportunities for all men, special privileges for none!" was Jefferson's ringing challenge.

One of his stanchest supporters was James Madison, now a Representative in Congress from Virginia. With Hamilton and

Thomas Jefferson's Republican Party is not to be confused with the Republican Party as we know it today.

John Jay of New York, Madison had written the *Federalist Papers*, but he wanted no aristocratic class in America. Always a champion of liberal causes, Madison had proposed amendments to the Constitution, guaranteeing to the people such basic rights as freedom of speech, assembly and worship. When enacted, these amendments were known as the Bill of Rights, the keystone of American democracy.

Somewhere between the two extremes of viewpoint, as if to balance them, was President Washington. At the time of his first election there had been no political parties. In his second election, the parties were still new, their lines scarcely drawn, and Washington was endorsed by the leaders of both.

Richard Lee and Aaron Burr belonged to the party of Thomas Jefferson and Madison. They believed that never again would a President be elected unanimously.

"The two-party system is entrenched now in this country," Lee said.

"Yes," said Senator Burr. "I think we shall have it through all our future history."

"Eliza, I'm invited to tea at the President's house," said Dolley on a snowy winter morning when her friend had dropped in for a chat. "See, a very proper, engraved card from Mrs. Washington. For Friday afternoon. Strange, isn't it, that she should ask me?"

"Why?" Elizabeth said. "Your sister Lucy is her niece-in-law. You're almost a *kin* of the Washingtons. And a Virginian, to boot. Oh, you Virginians are such a clannish lot! Mrs. Washington entertains at tea on most Fridays while Congress is in session. I'm going to this one, and so must you, Dolley. The diversion will be good for you."

Dolley scanned the card. "I am tempted — "

"Do go, Sister," Anna said. "I want you to. I'll sit with Payne."

They went in the Collins' sleigh that Friday afternoon, with the coachman up on the box and a bearskin rug tucked around them. Other sleighs and sleds were skimming toward the President's house, bells on the harness of the horses tinkled merrily in the sparkling cold sunshine. When Dolley and Elizabeth were in the house and had put off their coats, a liveried footman ushered them into a room that seemed overcrowded with fashionably dressed ladies.

"Dolley, our drab Quaker garb isn't the thing at all!" Elizabeth whispered, giggling. "We're a couple of dowdy sparrows straying among exotic-plumaged peafowls."

"But what a treat just to look at the peafowls!" Dolley said. "Lucy would describe this as a *squeeze*."

"So it is. The house is too small for it. Mrs. Washington must find these quarters cramped and inconvenient after her lovely home at Mount Vernon."

Mrs. Washington was standing at the end of the room to greet her guests. She was a rather plump little woman, with a pleasant, placid face and fine hazel-colored eyes. She wore a lacy cap, lace mitts and a gown of lavender silk, a fichu of cloth of silver at her throat. As she shook hands with Dolley, she inquired about Lucy, her nephew's wife, and then about Dolley's mother.

"I am told that your mother is living with the young Washingtons at Harewood. I trust they are making her comfortable there."

"Very comfortable, thank you," Dolley answered.

Mrs. Washington mentioned the Virginia Dandridges, Mrs.

Patrick Henry and Mr. Jefferson. "The Jeffersons were neighbors of your mother's people long ago in Albemarle County, were they not?"

"Yes," Dolley said, and thought to herself that Virginians were indeed like a clan, so many of them related by ties of blood or marriage or old neighborliness.

"And I suppose you have encountered Mr. James Madison in Philadelphia?" Mrs. Washington asked.

"No, never. Of course, I've heard a great deal about Mr. Madison."

"His estate, Montpellier, is in Orange County; but as a member of Congress, he maintains a residence in this city. Probably you will meet him sometime — though Mr. Madison is a bachelor of studious habits and does not often forsake his books."

With a smile, Mrs. Washington waved Dolley and Elizabeth on toward the flower-decked table where they were served with tea and slices of plum cake.

"Delicious cake!" Elizabeth said, nibbling and sipping. "Made from the famous Mount Vernon recipe book. You saw that our hostess shook hands with everybody? The President won't do that, when he comes."

"Oh, is the President coming, Eliza?"

"I think he shows himself briefly at all of Mrs. Washington's receptions."

"That will be something to tell Anna."

"But he never shakes anyone's hand, because he feels that the Presidency of the United States is the most exalted position in the world, and he's in duty bound to uphold its dignity." Elizabeth craned her neck. "Ah, here he is now."

The President entered quietly, bowing to the ladies and murmuring a polite phrase or two. His clothes were of black velvet, his waistcoat richly frilled; the stockings on his shapely legs were of thick black silk. An austere and commanding figure, he went to stand beside his wife, his grave countenance softening and creasing into a faint smile as he looked down at her.

"You know, Eliza, the Presidency *is* the most exalted position in the world," Dolley said, "and George Washington fills it nobly!"

At dusk they took their leave and were whirled homeward in the sleigh through shadowy, snow-banked streets. Somehow they fell to talking about Mr. James Madison, whom Dolley had never seen.

"He's not much to look at," Elizabeth said. "You may have seen him and just not noticed. He was once engaged to a Philadelphia girl — she jilted him. The story is that she sent Mr. Madison a letter, breaking the engagement, and sealed it with a lump of rye bread dough. For some reason, the lump of dough was thought of as a prime insult. I don't know that the girl meant it to be. She may have had no sealing wax on her desk at the moment, and the dough was right there, so she used it. At any rate, the story goes that Mr. Madison was terribly angry, and has never so much as glanced at a woman since!" . . .

But perhaps the story was exaggerated in some of its details — for one day in the spring Dolley, at her own desk, dashed off a hurried missive to Elizabeth: "Dear Friend, Thee must come to me. Aaron Burr says that the 'great little Madison' has asked to be brought to see me this evening."

Then she dusted her parlor, put bouquets of tulips and narcissus in her crystal vases, and trimmed the lamp wicks. She got out her best gown; it was a new one, the material was mulberry satin. Buying it, she had felt rather guilty — though nowadays Quaker ladies did wear this soft, subdued purplish hue — the rules allowed it, and she knew that she looked well in it. She got out her best white kerchief and cap — a widow's cap, but made of the daintiest Swiss voile, with loops of ribbon.

Anna watched these hurried preparations. "Will it be an unusual evening, Sister?"

"Not at all," Dolley said. "Just Senator Burr and another gentleman calling."

But she could not rid herself of the feeling that it might be the most unusual evening in her life.

8

MR. MADISON

When James Madison met Dolley Todd he was forty-three, a distinguished and wealthy man — but, as Elizabeth Collins had commented, not imposing looking. Of less than average height, he was very thin and dressed plainly and inconspicuously. His eyes were a clear blue, his features were clean cut and sensitive; but his face was pale, and he was already getting to be a bit bald, the brown hair receding from his brow.

He was the oldest child of his parents, and their mainstay. The management of the Madison plantation in Orange County was wholly in his hands. He had many brothers and sisters; they called him "Jemmy," and he was devoted to them all and to their children, his nieces and nephews. His ancestry was English; his forefathers had emigrated as pioneers to Virginia. Among the Virginians were Indian fighters and scouts — also magistrates and scholars. He had inherited traits from both of these contrasting strains.

As a boy, he had been delicate. Ill health had prevented his enjoying most sports and athletics, though he was a fine horseman. His early education was obtained from tutors at home. At the age of seventeen he had gone to Princeton College, in New Jersey, where Aaron Burr was a fellow student. At twenty he was graduated from Princeton, but then went back for a year of more intensive study in foreign languages.

Very young he had started a career of service to his native state and his country, and had been singularly successful. He was warmhearted and idealistic and made friends easily. He was calm, intelligent and just; therefore he made few enemies. He cared little for social festivities, but was not shy or self-conscious, and he possessed a whimsical humor, a gift for telling anecdotes that sometimes sent his listeners off into roars of laughter.

It had been said of "Jemmy" Madison that he might lack the physical vigor of an athlete, but he had a prodigiously vigorous mind and will — a way of attaining his goal.

And his goal now, it seemed, was to marry Dolley Todd. His courtship began with their introduction.

Elizabeth Collins had responded promptly to Dolley's appeal that spring evening. She came and brought Mr. Lee with her. They were five in the tidy, lamplit parlor. Their conversation was casual. Senator Burr was clever and amusing, as always; he paid graceful compliments to the ladies; he and Mr. Lee talked politics. Mr. Madison was mostly silent, but smiling. His eyes were on Dolley and, as he bade her good-night, he asked if he might come again.

"Soon?" he said. "Tomorrow?"

Thereafter scarcely a day went by that he did not come to

see her, if only for a half-hour, a moment. Very soon he asked her to marry him.

What was she to do? She thought about it earnestly; in a flutter of uncertainty she examined her feelings, her wishes.

Of course, she had not forgotten John Todd, her love for John and her grief at his death. Her marriage to John had been very suitable — everyone had said so, her family had been pleased by it. For those three years, nearly four, she had been quietly happy with John and, when she lost him so suddenly and tragically, she had felt for a time that her life was shattered. Then, returning from Gray's Ferry with the epidemic survivors, she had known that she was destined to go on living — in all likelihood for many years! — and that she must not be cowardly about shouldering the burdens that living laid upon her.

In the months since John's death the memories of her former happiness had sustained her; but she was only twenty-six and when she looked ahead, the future seemed to stretch long and difficult — and finally very lonely. She had Anna and Payne now, for a while she would have them, but not always. No, Anna would marry and go to a home of her own. Payne would grow up, go away to school, become a youth and then a man, quite independent of her. And this was right, of course. Such changes were inevitable and she was not so selfish as to want to keep either of them, or any young person, tied to her apron strings. Still, she could imagine how desolate she would be without them. She had never liked being alone!

And here was Mr. Madison eager for her to be his wife. What must she say to him? How hard it was to make up her mind! In deciding to marry John Todd, she had been influenced to some extent by the wishes and advice of other people — but nobody was urging her to marry James Madison except the gentleman himself. She knew that he was a good man, in all things worthy. He would be a fond and faithful husband, and would act as a loving father to Payne. She was very much attracted to Mr. Madison — but he was not a Quaker.

Whenever her reflections reached this point, Dolley sighed.

No, James Madison was not a Quaker. By marrying him, she would forfeit her membership in the Society of Friends. The Society's discipline was unbending, and Dolley had been taught that it was never wrong. Her mother believed in it; her father, even in his bitterest sorrow, had said that *he* was wrong, not the Society. It was necessary for the Society to have rules, and members must abide by them.

Sighing, Dolley knew how Lucy must have felt in defying the rules. And Eliza Collins, too. Indeed, love is no respecter of persons!

Spring came and then summer, and still Dolley was doubtful. In June Eliza married Richard Lee and they sailed for a honeymoon in England. Congress adjourned, Mr. Madison left Philadelphia to spend the vacation with his parents at Montpellier.

The city seemed dull and unnaturally empty.

"I'll tell you what we'll do, Anna," Dolley said. "We'll take a trip down into Virginia, you and Payne and I."

"To Scotchtown?" Anna asked.

"No. I'd like to see Scotchtown, but strangers are there now. We'll visit some of Mother's relatives, the Coles. And we'll go to see Mother and Lucy and all the dear people at Harewood."

"Oh, Mama, will we ride in a stagecoach?" Payne cried, skipping and frolicking.

"Yes, darling," she said. "In lots of stagecoaches."

They rode in the stagecoaches and were welcomed by the

Coles relatives — but it was a rather depressing summer. In August they turned wearily toward Harewood. The day was hot, the drive tedious; they stopped to change coaches at Fredericksburg.

"We have an hour to wait," Dolley said. "We'll go into the hotel."

"I'm thirsty!" Payne wailed. "I want a drink!"

Dolley gave her purse to Anna. "Here, buy the child a lemonade. And one for yourself, too."

Anna and Payne went to get their cooling drink, and Dolley sat down at a desk in the hotel passage. She had been thinking of James Madison; suddenly all her doubts had fled and she knew what she wished to do. The note she wrote to him was hurried but definite. She said that she was on her way to Lucy Washington's home — and that she would marry him.

The wedding in September, at Harewood, was attended by Dolley's mother and sisters, the Washington household and a dozen or more close friends. Lucy had filled the rooms of the fine old mansion with autumn flowers from her garden, and twined the beautiful staircase with ferns and smilax. The ceremony was performed by Dr. Alexander Balmaine, an Episcopal clergyman and a cousin of Madison's.

The bridegroom was in exuberant spirits. He had brought Dolley a necklace of rare medallions in exquisite mosaic work to wear with her mulberry gown. And for this occasion he had dressed himself in gala attire — silk coat, breeches and stockings, and an embroidered waistcoat with a flowing jabot of Mechlin lace.

The young lady guests joked with Mr. Madison about the

magnificent jabot, which made him laugh lightheartedly. Later, at the supper table, he allowed Lucy to fetch a pair of scissors and snip off pieces of the lace, and these he distributed as souvenirs.

After supper, while the company lingered on, Dolley ran upstairs to scribble a few lines to her "dearest Eliza" in England.

"This day I give my hand to the man whom of all others I most admire," she confided. "In this union I have everything that is soothing and grateful in prospect — and my little Payne will have a generous and tender protector."

In October the Madisons, with Payne and Anna, returned to Philadelphia, where James leased a house for them. Almost immediately Dolley was notified that the Pine Street Quakers had expelled her from their Society because of her marriage to "a person not in membership with us, before a hireling priest."

"Oh, Sister, how dreadful," Anna said.

"I expected it," Dolley said. "The Society wastes no time. Eliza Lee got her dismissal three months ago. I'm sorry to have offended the Friends — I would wish never to offend anyone — but I'm not sorry I married James, for with every day he's dearer to me."

The Madisons had come back to a turmoil of politics. Many Americans were convinced that a second war with England impended. England, it seemed, had never believed that the Revolution was conclusive, but had continued to think of the United States as her colonies which had gone astray, escaped — and must be retaken. There had been recurrent disputes about the boundary between Canada and the northern states. On one pretext or another, British soldiers had remained in American territory; in the rapidly growing West they had stirred up the Indians to raid and pillage pioneer American settlements. In several instances, England had interfered with America's shipping trade, stopping American ships at sea and impressing the sailors into service on British ships, with the charge that they were runaway subjects of the English king.

Hoping to adjust these thorny difficulties peaceably, President Washington sent John Jay to London as a special envoy to negotiate a treaty. But when the provisions of Jay's treaty were known in America, there were loud denunciations from every section. Newspaper editorials savagely attacked John Jay, accusing him of having yielded all the advantages to England and humiliated his own country. Mobs of enraged citizens hanged him in effigy. The Federalist leader, Alexander Hamilton, was stoned as he mounted a public platform to defend both Jay and the treaty; and the British minister in Philadelphia, fearing for his life, skulked in the cellar of his home.

Men of Thomas Jefferson's party said that Washington would never sign a compact so hampering to American commerce and development. "Washington will never sign it!" they said. But in this they were mistaken. Though Washington saw the faults of Jay's treaty, he was unwilling to risk a second war with England, one that perhaps the United States could not win. He signed — and most Americans shook their heads ominously, predicting that the second war had only been postponed.

As James Madison's wife, Dolley was plunged into the very midst of this political storm, and also into a brisk social activity quite new to her. Madison's friends had heard of the young and beautiful Mrs. Madison, but few of them knew her. Now they plied her with invitations to luncheons, dinners and balls.

"James, what am I to do with all these invitations?" she asked, eying the heaped-up basket of cards.

"Accept them, of course," he said.

"I've never gone out much, you know."

"I'm proud of you, Dolley. I want my friends to meet you. I'll even escort you to the gaieties — some of them. But you must have the clothes for it. Your pretty Quaker gowns can be put aside, or worn in the house of mornings. Do you like to shop?"

"I've had very little experience at that," she said. "James, I was seventeen before I ever went into a dressmaker's shop. And then it was only to *look,* not to buy anything."

"Well, now you must buy, too," he said, his eyes twinkling.

So Dolley went shopping. She bought satins, foulards and brocades, feathers, reticules, gloves and slippers. The Philadelphia dressmakers and milliners soon were saying that Mrs. Madison had an instinctive good taste, always knowing the styles and colors most becoming to her. At any social gathering, the ladies looked to see what Mrs. Madison was wearing. Such striking costumes! they said, smart hats and bonnets, gowns that seemed molded to her tall, erect figure.

And one day she brought home a parrot.

"A parrot!" Madison exclaimed, gingerly inspecting the bird.

"I've wanted one for years, Jemmy. Eliza Lee will vouch for that."

"Does it bite?"

"No, it's a civilized fowl."

"I trust so." He laughed. "I suppose you'll teach it to sing."

"If I can," she said. "Payne and I will give it singing lessons. How lovely if we could teach it to sing 'Just like yonder rose!'"

That winter for the first time in her life, Dolley assumed the duties of a hostess. James Madison was a popular man and he enjoyed entertaining his friends. Though he ate and drank sparingly, he was an excellent judge of food and wine. He liked to have people in for dinner, and he did not confine his guest list to those who sided with him politically, for he was not averse to hearing both sides of any question. He wanted his home to be a place where people could mingle congenially in a restful atmosphere.

"And that's what you've made it, Dolley," he said. "You have been quick to learn the art of entertaining."

"Is it an art?" she said. "I think not. You see, Jemmy, people interest me. I'm — well, *curious*, I want to know all about them. Most people are so worth knowing!"

Madison smiled. "My colleagues in Congress are saying that the sun has shone on me, Dolley, that I have got an exceptionally amiable helpmate and spouse. And that's quite true."

In September, 1796, the election year, George Washington announced that he would not be a candidate for a third term in the Presidency. The announcement, afterward to be known as his Farewell Address, was in the form of a lengthy message published in the newspapers. Washington was sixty-four. For most of his life he had zealously and unselfishly served his countrymen — and was, he said, their "old and affectionate friend." But the time had come, he said, for him to retire.

By the election methods provided for in the Constitution, the Presidential candidate who received the highest number of votes was elected to the office, the candidate receiving the next highest number of votes became Vice-President. As a result of Washington's withdrawal from the 1796 contest, John Adams, a Federalist of Massachusetts, was named to the Presidency, with

Thomas Jefferson, the Virginia Republican, as Vice-President.

Dolley and her sister Anna were spectators at the inauguration of John Adams in the House of Representatives on March 4, 1797. From their bench in the gallery, they looked down at the large audience.

"There's James," Dolley said, "seated with the other Congressmen."

"Is that Mrs. Washington in the front row?" Anna asked.

"Yes, with Mrs. Adams beside her."

"How solemn everyone is — "

"Hush!" Dolley said. "The President is coming."

Adams and Washington entered the room together: Adams short and stout, ruddy faced, in a coat of bright green cloth with cuffs of white linen; Washington in his usual black velvet, his powdered hair tied behind with a black ribbon, his sword in a green scabbard at his belt, a black three-cornered hat with black silk cockade carried in the crook of his arm.

The crowd was silent until Washington began to speak, then many people wept and some sobbed aloud.

"Oh, see Mr. Adams," Anna whispered. "He's weeping, too."

Dolley glanced at John Adams. His head was bowed in his hands; tears dropped through his fingers to spot his white cuffs.

When Adams had recited the oath of office, the audience filed out to the street, but did not disperse. Washington emerged from the building and the crowd fell into step behind him. He went to the Indian Queen Hotel to pay a formal call on the new President and Mrs. Adams; in silence the crowd went with him all the way.

On March 9, the Washingtons in their yellow coach drove out of Philadelphia, bound for Mount Vernon, and again hundreds of people were in the street to see them go. But Dolley and Anna were not there. They were busily packing portmanteaus and satchels that day, for Madison had resigned his seat in Congress and the Madisons also were leaving the city.

"Adams is President, the Federalists are in power," Madison had said. "For the next four years, I shall be a gentleman farmer at Montpellier."

"And afterward, Jemmy?" Dolley queried.

He smiled and said, "Who knows?"

9

MONTPELLIER

Montpellier, in Orange County, was an estate of four thousand acres. The square brick house stood on a knoll, its long French windows looking out to the forested slopes of the Blue Ridge Mountains. Around it were orchards and vegetable gardens, meadows in which herds of cattle grazed, and broad fields planted in tobacco, wheat and corn.

Like most wealthy Southerners, the Madisons were slave-owners. Though Madison himself hated the institution of slavery and would have favored any workable scheme for emancipation, he did not think that to free the Negroes at Montpellier would correct an evil so deep rooted and general. He believed with Thomas Jefferson that someday there would have to be a reformation, all the chains broken. Meanwhile, he would concentrate on being the best possible master to his slaves, as his father had been before him.

Dolley knew that Madison's parents were old. She had wondered how they might feel about his marriage.

"They have leaned on you," she said to him. "You've been a prop to them. Perhaps they thought that you would never marry. They may feel that I'm an interloper. They may not want me here, or Payne, or Anna, any or all of us."

But these fears were groundless. From the moment of their meeting, the elder Madisons gave Dolley their affection and trust, they liked Anna at once — and exclaimed over Payne.

How good it was to have a boy in the house again! they said. And what a sturdy fellow this one was, so tall for his age!

"He must have a pony, James," said Madison's father, stroking Payne's brown curls.

"Yes, indeed. I've told him that. And a dog, kittens."

"Guinea pigs?" Payne said.

"Every kind of pet there is," Madison promised, smiling.

Madison had plans for remodeling the house and he discussed them with Dolley. He would add wings to the original square structure, face the bricks with Virginia stone and build a classic portico. A flower garden with curving paths and a fountain would be laid out for Dolley. The remodeling would take time.

"But life is always leisurely at Montpellier," he said.

It did seem to Dolley that the days had a steady, even flow, melting imperceptibly into weeks and months. The plantation was like a small-scale self-contained world. Within its area were a mill, a blacksmith's shop, a carpentry shop, a laundry, sheds for curing meat, cellars for storing fruit, wine and ice, kilns in which bricks were burnt.

Madison had a fine stable and often raced his thoroughbred horses at nearby tracks. He bought a shaggy Shetland pony for

Payne, and gentle mounts for Dolley and Anna to ride. His own
horse was a spirited bay, and every morning of fair weather he
led them all in a before-breakfast canter about the fields and
woods.

No season passed that there were not visitors in the big house,
scores of them during the summer and the Christmas holidays.
At Easter the George Steptoe Washingtons came from Harewood, bringing Dolley's mother, her brother Johnnie and her
sister Mary.

"I shall keep Mary at Montpellier for a month or so," Dolley
said to Lucy. "Isn't she pretty? Mary will be company for
Anna. I think Anna rather misses the excitements of the city.
Well, I miss them, too — rather. But this is better for Payne.
He loves the farm."

"You know, Dolley, Payne is a bit willful and naughty,"
Lucy said. "Don't you ever scold him?"

"No, of course not!"

"And James never scolds him?"

"James adores him."

"When my youngsters are naughty, I tell them about it," Lucy
said. "I think Payne should have more contacts with other children. He's with adults too much, and you all humor his slightest wish."

Dolley looked thoughtfully at Lucy. "Perhaps you're right.
I want to do everything I can for my son."

"And I suppose you never forget how stern Father was with
us, when we were little?" Lucy said. "Yes, I used to think that
Father was an ogre. But there's a safe path between that sort of
sternness and overindulgence, isn't there?"

Dolley assented meekly. "You must be right, Lucy. I'll try to
find it."

Thomas Jefferson frequently visited at Montpellier, and Dolley and James went several times a year to Monticello, Jefferson's house in Albemarle County. Jefferson had been the sole architect, builder and decorator of Monticello; he had filled it with his ingenious inventions: a wonderful clock that showed the days of the week and had two dials, one inside of the house and one outside; a swivel chair, a folding ladder, a dumbwaiter concealed in the dining room mantel, a bed that could be lifted by pulleys to the ceiling when not needed.

Dolley was fascinated by the thousands of books in Jefferson's library — and by the man himself, his intellect and great integrity, his simple manners. Jefferson hated all tyranny, particularly the tyranny which would have controlled the minds of human beings and molded them into a pattern. His concern was for the common people; he fought an endless battle for the poor and underprivileged of his country and every country.

In appearance he was very tall, loose jointed and wiry, with sandy hair and keen gray eyes. He gave little thought to his clothing as long as it was clean and comfortable. He was a widower; his children, two daughters, were both married. When not traveling, or on government business in Philadelphia, he lived alone with his servants in his beautiful house.

Dolley knew of Jefferson's warm friendship for her husband; she was glad that he quickly included her in it.

"I remember your mother," he said to her, when the Madisons visited Monticello soon after their marriage. "Mary Coles. Yes, she was a belle in Albemarle County. You are very like her."

Softly and tranquilly the months drifted by — and then were marred by a letter reaching Dolley from a stranger down in the western region of Virginia.

Temple and Isaac Payne had been killed in an accident.

Or was it an accident? Dolley did not know. The letter was mysterious in tone. Isaac, it seemed, had got embroiled with a trespasser while he and Temple were plowing their hilly property. The rumor was that Isaac had been drinking and was quarrelsome. The trespasser had a gun; he shot Isaac, wounding him. Temple had rushed to disarm the trespasser, wrested the gun from him. In the scuffle, more shots were fired; the brothers were fatally hurt and died.

Dolley mourned deeply for them. Once Temple had said that she never cried. But she cried now.

Though the Madisons lived quietly at Montpellier, they still were in touch with national affairs. James might declare his intention to be only a gentleman farmer, but he was often called to Philadelphia, or statesmen came to the plantation to confer with him, and Dolley heard a great deal about the new capital city that was rising on the bank of the Potomac River.

This city was to be a realization of the dream of many Americans. Perhaps Washington and Jefferson had been the first to perceive that the new United States must have a splendid, permanent capital. In 1788, through Jefferson's efforts, ten square miles of land on the Potomac had been ceded to Congress by the state of Maryland as a site for the capital. Washington had surveyed the land and selected the exact location for the city.

Congress had then appointed Pierre Charles L'Enfant to draw the city plans. L'Enfant, a Frenchman by birth, had been an officer in the American army during the Revolution. He was an artist as well as an architect. His artist's eye conjured up a noble design — a domed Capitol building on a hill, with wide avenues radiating from it like spokes of a wheel, perpendicular streets crisscrossing the avenues, symmetrical office buildings and a President's House with the gracious proportions of a southern mansion.

When L'Enfant got his design on paper, a board of commissioners was appointed to undertake the direction of the engineers, stonemasons and carpenters. The work went slowly, for the expenses were enormous; there was never much money available and sometimes none at all.

The city was to be named for Washington. Pleased by this tribute paid to him by his countrymen, Washington made daily trips from Mount Vernon to check on the builders' progress. He saw one wing of the Capitol completed and the President's House roofed over. The date set for the transferring of the United States government from Philadelphia to the city on the Potomac was early in 1800 — a date which Washington did not live to see.

On December 14, 1799, in towns and villages, everywhere, the church bells tolled and tolled all day. George Washington was dead.

The Adamses were the first Presidential family to occupy the house L'Enfant had designed, and they did not like it. Or the new city, either! John Adams thought that the national capital should have remained at Philadelphia, which was civilized, cultured, convenient. This place was an undrained marsh, a frog pond, surrounded by a wilderness — and would be for years! Mrs. Adams said the President's House was huge, drafty, cold as a barn. Her furniture looked dwarfed in it, she would have needed twenty times as many lamps to light it properly. Not a single room entirely finished. . . . "The great audience room I make a drying room of, to hang up the clothes in," Mrs. Adams wrote to her daughter in Boston.

But Mrs. Adams was not to be bothered very long, for John Adams had not been re-elected. In the 1800 election, the Republicans had won the Presidency — though most oddly, with their two candidates, Thomas Jefferson and Aaron Burr, polling the same number of votes.

What was to be done about this?

At Montpellier, the Madisons talked of the predicament. It was a November night, chill and frosty. Madison sat in an armchair at the fireside; Dolley, on a stool, was knitting a scarf of orange wool.

"What will happen now, James?" she asked.

"The Constitution says that, in the case of a tie, the election goes to the House of Representatives," he answered. "The Representatives will vote on the tied candidates. The one who gets a majority of their votes will then have been elected President, the other contender will have to eat humble pie, as Vice-President."

"It doesn't seem a very good way," Dolley said.

"It isn't. I think the Constitution will have to be amended. That can be done. Our Constitution is far from perfect, but its redeeming feature is that it can be changed as conditions in the country change."

Dolley's needles flashed in the firelight. "Whom will the Representatives elect, James?"

"Jefferson, I think. Of course, it's in Alexander Hamilton's hands now."

"Mr. Hamilton? Why? Mr. Hamilton isn't a Representative, he won't be voting."

"No, but the Federalist Representatives will vote as Hamilton decrees, and I think it will be for Jefferson. Not that Hamilton has any love for Tom Jefferson. Oh, no! But he knows that Jefferson is a man of honor, whereas he detests Aaron Burr and suspects him of being unscrupulous."

"Unscrupulous?" Dolley repeated, puzzled. "Do you think that about Senator Burr?"

"No," Madison said. "Burr is arrogant and ambitious, he always was. His tendency is to chase the rainbow of fame, but I have never had cause to distrust him."

"Well, I've *liked* him," Dolley said. "I feel that I owe him my eternal thanks for bringing us together, Jemmy."

Madison smiled. "I do not forget that, my dear — though if Aaron hadn't done so, I should have found someone else to introduce me. I had known you by sight for a long time, and I was determined to meet you."

She was silent a moment. "I suppose Mr. Jefferson would make a better President than Senator Burr."

"Better than anybody! Jefferson is the best we have."

"When will it all be settled?"

"Maybe not for weeks. The Representatives will convene in February to ballot, and there's sure to be much stubborn wrangling among them." Madison laughed, and added: "How disgusted Hamilton's Federalists will be at having to vote for any Republican!"

The Representatives assembled February 11, in the unfinished Capitol building in Washington — which was as yet a raw, unkempt village, snow covered now, the snow stretching in a smooth white sheet to the Potomac's icy brink. For five days

they balloted, and it was not until the sixth day and the thirty-
sixth ballot that Thomas Jefferson was elected to the Presidency
by the scant margin of two votes.

Jefferson was inaugurated on March 4, and announced that
James Madison would be his Secretary of State.

So the Madisons were going to Washington!

"I have mixed feelings about it," Dolley said to Anna. "I'm
glad to have James so recognized, but I have loved plantation
life. Of course, we'll spend the summers at Montpellier. That
will be something to look forward to!"

10

WASHINGTON HOSTESS

The heavy old-fashioned carriage rumbled along the narrow road, then into an unpaved street sparsely bordered with houses and stores. It was midafternoon, the first day of May, the last lap of a tiresome journey. The horses were sweating, the wheels of the carriage were thick with dust. Inside, on the dust-filmed cushions, Dolley and Anna swayed drowsily, and Payne dozed, his head against Madison's shoulder.

"We're here, Dolley," Madison said. "This is Pennsylvania Avenue."

"Really? Are we really here?" Dolley straightened and peered from the window. "Why, it doesn't look such a wild and barren place at all!"

"It's fast building up, very fast. And a good thing," Madison said. "There were many people, like John Adams, who called it the 'City of Miserable Huts' and thought of it as an absolute folly."

"But Mr. Adams was vexed about nearly everything, James."

"Yes. Alas, poor John! The fact that he had been defeated for a second term as President rankled in his breast. When he saw Jefferson, he burst forth wrathfully: 'You have turned me out! You have turned me out!' And he would not stay for the inauguration, but hurried away in the darkness at four o'clock that morning. Adams is an honest man, he was a conscientious Chief Executive, but he is not sweet tempered or a good loser."

"I can see twenty or more houses," Dolley said. "Quite new looking. And a grocery, a tailor's shop, a printer's. Oh, and a stationer's store — "

"A shoemaker's shop, a cloth merchant's emporium," said Madison.

Anna opened her eyes and yawned. "Is it a game?" she asked. "Let me play."

"We're viewing the capital, Anna, and it's very nice," Dolley said. "James, surely that's a fish and oyster market yonder."

"Oh, oysters!" Anna said, "I love them. Have you listed the dozen old colonial houses we passed just a while back?"

"Those were in Georgetown," said Madison. "I thought you were sleeping when we drove through Georgetown."

Anna laughed. "Half sleeping — and half seeing, with one eye. And what is this big pile of gray stone, James?"

"The President's House, our destination. Wake up, Payne!" Madison gently shook the boy's arm. "Wake up, son. Yes, we're really here."

President Jefferson was at the door to greet the Madisons, for they were to be his guests until they could get lodgings elsewhere. A suite of rooms had been made ready for them. When their luggage was unloaded and they had refreshed themselves with tea and biscuits, he suggested that Dolley might like to inspect this big pile of gray stone.

"And tell me frankly what you think of it, Dolley," he said. "I know your talents as a housekeeper."

"I fear they're my only talents, Mr. Jefferson."

"A woman could have none finer," he said, with a bow.

The architect for the house had been James Hoban, a young Irishman. As Jefferson showed Dolley about, he explained that there had been a public competition, the newspapers advertising for architects to submit blueprints of a house in which the President would live. A committee of judges had adopted Hoban's plan and awarded the prize to him.

"With your approval?" Dolley asked.

"I did have something to say in the matter. I liked Hoban's drawings, the size and plain contours of the house, the stone columns at the front, and the balustraded roof. The building may be altered as time goes on, altered and enlarged; it probably will be. But I thought Hoban's design was the one to start with."

Jefferson had furnished twenty-three of the numerous rooms.

"And mostly with things from Monticello!" Dolley said. "These are the Monticello chairs and tables, bureaus and sofas, aren't they?"

"Yes. The Adamses had only a little furniture here, and took that little with them. When I came, the house was empty as a shell. I had some things carted up from the plantation. Several of my servants were coming anyway, my butler and cook, the coachman and stableboys; they drove the carts. They thought it was all quite a lark — and I should have been very homesick without a few of my Monticello people around me."

"But the chintz curtains," Dolley said. "They are new."

"Yes. I bought the curtains and the carpets."

"Out of your own pocket, I'll wager!"

He nodded. "Do you like them?"

"They're just right," Dolley said. "The colors blend so softly."

"Of course, much is still to be done," he said, as they went from room to room. "Perhaps you'll advise me now and then."

"You've made a fine beginning," she said. "I shall be happy to do anything I can."

That evening six government officials and their wives came to dine with the President. He had courteously seated Dolley at his right hand. He seemed to watch her thoughtfully, and he smiled when the lady at his left said to him in an undertone: "Mrs. Madison is so charming and affable. One cannot but be at ease in her presence."

"Yes, yes," Jefferson murmured. "The Madisons are old friends of mine, you know. They are — like homefolks."

Later, when the dinner guests had gone, Dolley knocked at the door of Anna's bedroom. She had on the dress of turquoise dotted swiss she had worn at dinner, but had taken off the ribbon sash and her beaded hair ornaments.

"Will you unhook me, Anna?" she said. "The hooks on my bodice are so tiny, I can't get at them."

"Come in," Anna said, "and hold still. There now! You're not quite so slim as you were, Dolley."

"I'm older, darling. In a week, I shall be thirty-three. Heavens, a great age, isn't it?"

"Do you worry about it?"

"No, what would be the good of that?"

Anna sat down on the bed. In her robe of pink flannel and

ruched nightcap, she looked sweet and demure. "You ought to have a maid, Dolley?"

"Yes, I should have brought Sukey Jennings from Montpellier. Sukey is the dearest thing, and she wanted to come. James says I may send for her when we get a house. And we must write to Sister Mary and have her come to us from Harewood for one of her long visits. Wouldn't that be fun, Anna? And when Congress is in session again, in the fall, Washington will be swarming with eligible bachelors, and I shall get you and Mary each a most superior husband."

Anna laughed. "As superior as James Madison?"

"No, I could never do that well by you! It's expecting too much."

"Dolley, I've been thinking about Mr. Jefferson — "

"Rather elderly for you, isn't he?"

"Oh, *silly!*" Anna said. "Mr. Jefferson is *antiquated.*"

"Fifty-eight, I believe. I daresay it does seem antiquated to you."

"I mean," Anna said, "that tonight at the table I was thinking about him — a lone man in this huge house, having to give dinners and receptions, as he *will* have to, and without any feminine assistance. He's so gracious, yet I feel that something is lacking here, something a woman could supply. I suppose I'm being terribly vague?"

"No." Dolley sat down beside her sister. "The same thought occurred to me this afternoon. Somehow I felt sorry for him."

"You know his daughters. What are they like? Perhaps they'll come to live in Washington."

"I shouldn't think so, Anna. Probably they'll spend what time they can with their father, for they're devoted to him. Their mother died when they were very small. Mr. Jefferson took them to France when he had to go abroad on a government mission, and put them into a French convent school, so that he would not be separated from them. But they are women now, married, with homes and families. Martha, the older one, is the wife of Thomas Mann Randolph, a Congressman from Virginia. She has a great many children. Martha Randolph is very bright, and she's had an amazingly thorough education, but she cares nothing for either politics or society. The younger daughter, Maria Eppes, is an invalid and is seldom to be seen anywhere."

"Well," Anna said musingly, "Mr. Jefferson will certainly need more feminine assistance than they seem likely to give him. I believe he may turn to you for it, Dolley. Isn't Vice-President Burr a widower also? And James will be the ranking cabinet member. I think you may find yourself helping with the official entertaining. You're the logical person for it, you know."

Dolley was surprised, she had never foreseen such obligations. But she repeated, rather humbly, what she had said to Mr. Jefferson earlier: "I shall be happy to do anything I can."

From Anna's room, she went to Payne's bedroom. He was asleep. By the light of a candle on the bureau, his face was revealed to her — a beautiful face, flushed with healthy color. But how big he looked lying there, his arms flung up over the pillows. He was growing at an alarming rate and was no longer a baby! Perhaps she should be thinking of sending him to school, one of the academies that prepared boys for college — Lucy would have said so. But Dolley pushed the thought away hastily. No, there was plenty of time for that! She would get a tutor for Payne. For a few more years, she would hold him close — before loosing the apron strings.

She bent and kissed him, then blew out the candle and went to open the window wider, for the night was warm. Standing at the window, she could see nothing of the city. Darkness obscured the scattered buildings, the lines that marked the avenues and streets of Pierre L'Enfant's pattern, most of which had yet to be constructed. From the swampy lowlands to the south came a distant chorus of hoarse, croaking sounds. She smiled to hear it. Frogs! Yes, the District of Columbia was still largely an undrained marsh, a frog pond, the nation's capital still only a dream in the minds of men.

But she respected the dream and knew that she, too, had faith in it. She was sure that this city would someday have a lofty grandeur and be ranked among the great cities of the world. And already she had a strange feeling of possessiveness about it — as if, because she was an American citizen, the city belonged in part to her!

It was several weeks before the Madisons found a house in Washington, and the one they rented then was small and poorly built.

Jefferson had wanted them to stay on with him, but James declined.

"Our Federalist friends are gossiping that the President of the United States is running a tavern," he said, smiling. "They conjecture as to how much you're charging for my family's accommodations here. No, we shall be going to Montpellier for July and August anyway, and I have an agent who swears he'll get us a proper dwelling in the autumn."

The house into which they moved in September was in F Street, near the President's House and the homes of other Cabinet members. The city was expanding and filling up, the Congressmen were all coming back. By Christmastime a social season had started in government circles.

Dolley had brought her maid, Sukey Jennings, and two menservants from Virginia, and now she issued invitations for a series of "evenings" to be given twice each month throughout the winter.

She wrote the cards very carefully, with little flourishes of the pen: "The Secretary of State and Mrs. Madison request the pleasure of your company . . ."

Her guests always arrived at the hour of eight. They chatted, listened to a program of music or recitations, had supper at a table glittering with silver and glass and whirled off in their carriages at just after ten. To Dolley herself the "evenings" were sincerely a pleasure; and the people who partook of her hospitality — the Senators and Representatives and their ladies, the envoys, ministers and distinguished visitors from foreign lands — praised them enthusiastically.

Never, they said, never had they tasted such food, such rare dishes, fluffy cakes and pastries. And *ice cream*, an exquisite dessert which Mrs. Madison had *invented!*

Dolley liked the compliments very well, she said that her mother had taught her to cook, but ice cream was not her invention.

"I make it from a recipe that Mr. Jefferson got in France," she said. "It's a novelty for which we must thank Mr. Jefferson. Nor am I the first to serve it in this country. Mrs. Washington has often served ice cream at Mount Vernon."

All that winter and the next the capital city was very gay; Dolley was invited everywhere — and often she was astonished at the amount of entertaining which seemed to be considered necessary to the business of government. She was modest about her own success as a hostess, and though rather bewildered by her popularity, she enjoyed it. But when someone ventured to remark that Mrs. Madison had become the capital's uncrowned queen, she quickly and scornfully disclaimed the title.

"A queen of any sort in our democracy? Absurd!" she said.

Occasionally in these years she was the official hostess at the President's House, lending Mr. Jefferson the "feminine assistance" of which Anna had spoken. Such functions were formal, stately and unexciting. But sometimes she was appealed to in an emergency. In the late afternoon she would receive a hurried message from Mr. Jefferson: his cook was down with ague, his butler had toothache, no marketing had been done, he had just discovered that there wasn't a thing fit to eat in the larder — and ten Senators coming to dine with him!

Then Dolley would marshal her wits and call to Sukey Jennings. "What have we on hand, Sukey? A ham? A turkey? Good! Put them into the carriage, and fetch a few bottles of Mr. Madison's wine. We're going to the President's House, you and I. We'll creep in through the side door, so that no one sees us."

The interval that followed would be rushed and anxious, yet it was rewarding, too, with Dolley directing the activity, like a stage manager behind the scenes. When order was restored, the ham and turkey baking in the oven, the wine cooling in an ice bucket, the butler's toothache relieved, the cook dosed with calomel, Dolley and Sukey would creep out, quiet as mice, through the side door and go home to F Street, feeling tired but satisfied with their accomplishments.

Jolting over the rutted roads to and from Montpellier in the spring and fall gradually demolished the Madisons' coach.

"We must have a new conveyance," James said.

The "chariot" he bought had windows all around, boxed wheels and oil lamps. The interior was equipped with Venetian blinds and fringed, fawn-brown upholstery. The doors were embossed with a silver *M*, and the harness of the horses was silver plated.

In the chariot Dolley drove about Washington, usually with Payne and Anna, and with Mary also when this younger sister came from Harewood for visits. They made quite a picture, people said — the three pretty ladies ("the Three Graces from Virginia," according to one Washington gentleman's description) and the handsome, dark-haired boy. If Dolley saw any friend on foot, perhaps a Congressman toiling up the hill to the Capitol, she stopped the chariot and took him in.

"I notice, Dolley," said Anna, "that nobody ever refuses the ride!"

Frequently the ladies were headed for the shops. Dolley did not shop just for herself now. She had Anna and Mary to think of; yes, and Mr. Jefferson's daughters, when they visited their father. Mrs. Randolph and Mrs. Eppes were intelligent and of the most exemplary character, but they had no sense whatever about clothes. They were dowdy, and they knew it, and Mr. Jefferson knew it and had asked Dolley to get them some spruce and appropriate apparel.

As she shopped indefatigably, Dolley remembered with a smile how in Philadelphia she and Eliza Collins had pressed their noses to those forbidden windows and confessed their sinful yearnings. The styles for women were even more elaborate and lavish now. Enterprising merchants in American cities were importing costly and luxurious fabrics from Europe. Dressmakers earnestly studied the illustrated fashion magazines and displayed to their clients collections of wax dolls attired in the latest modes of London and Paris.

Dolley was now regarded as the most fashionable woman in Washington; and for the benefit of those who had not seen them, the costumes she wore to this or that social affair were reported in the newspapers:

... "Mrs. Madison had on a turban of white satin, with three large ostrich feathers hanging over her face, very becoming indeed! Her dress of white satin, made high in the neck with long sleeves and large capes trimmed with swan's down, was rich and beautiful. She carried a gold and enamel snuffbox."

... "Mrs. Madison's yellow satin gown was embroidered all over with butterflies in all colors. Her bonnet was white, with plumes."

... "The wife of Secretary Madison received at home in a white cambric gown, ruffled around the bottom, over her shoulders a peach-bloom scarf with rich border, a spencer of satin of the same color, a turban of peach-bloom gauze."

... "Mrs. Madison was in sky-blue striped velvet and lace, with a large ruff; a lace turban starred in gold, with white feather."

Dolley read the printed items and grimaced. "I do like finery," she said to Anna. "More than I should, perhaps; I daresay it's foolish of me. But I should have to be very conceited to think that my spencers and turbans deserve anyone else's notice."

"They're observed, talked about and copied," Anna said. "And you're not at all conceited. If you were, you couldn't have charmed so many people, women as well as men, and without causing a flicker of jealousy."

"Why, Anna!"

"Oh, yes. The things I hear! It's said you're not only beautiful, but a clever conversationalist with a lovely speaking voice. To some people, your manners seem polished and elegant, others see you as naïve and unaffected. There's something *bracing* about you — 'Mrs. Madison is a foe to dullness!' "

"Anna, you're laughing at me."

"I'm not. But I've watched you. How do you cast your spell? This town has scores of beautiful and clever women who are much less admired. I believe it's your courtesy to people of all kinds, whether or not you like them — and your willingness to sit and listen endlessly to the opinions of droning old bores."

"Heavens, what a strange creature you make me out!" Dolley said. "And how sad for the droning old bores if nobody ever listened to them. I may be one myself someday."

Anna shook her head. "No, Sister."

The red-letter events of the season's social calendar were the Dancing Assembly and the horse races. Dolley was a patroness of the Assembly. With Captain Thomas Tingey, a Navy officer, she made the arrangements for it, saw that an orchestra was obtained and planned the supper menu. But she did not dance.

"I was reared in the Quaker discipline," she told Captain Tingey. "I never learned to dance."

The races in November were like a vast picnic to which the whole city went, people of all ages and both sexes, everybody from the President to the lowliest bootblack. For those three days, work was forgotten, government business was suspended and Congress snatched at any flimsy excuse to adjourn. Dressed in their best and carrying furled parasols, Dolley and Anna drove out to the track in the Madison chariot. They had a hamper of lunch with them, pastries and preserved fruit, a carafe of sweetened cold tea.

Madison had gone earlier, to mark a place for them in the row of carriages that faced the oval of green turf. Dolley and Anna stepped down from their fawn-brown cushions, opened their parasols and sauntered about, nodding and smiling to their friends.

President Jefferson and other gentlemen were on horseback, trotting around the track, pausing at the paddock to confer with the jockeys who would ride in their silks.

"There's James!" Dolley cried, as Madison galloped his horse past them.

"Does he see us?" Anna asked.

"Oh, yes, he's waving his hat."

Sometimes Madison's thoroughbred, Wild Medley, raced — and more than once Wild Medley won! Dolley was very proud then, clapping her hands so vigorously that she burst the seams of her gloves.

11

EVENTFUL YEARS

George Washington had felt that the President of the United States should hold himself aloof from the people. John Adams had asserted that the President should be addressed as "Your Highness," and his home known as "the Palace." But Thomas Jefferson scoffed at this reserve and dignity. It was artificial nonsense, he said. He wanted no royal honors. Citizens wishing to see him could do so at any time, his door was always open to them. As President, he was the servant of the people.

His clothing was just as it had been at Monticello: a plain blue coat and waistcoat, velveteen breeches, yarn stockings, leather-strapped shoes — no gold braid or buttons, tassels or jeweled buckles. He never powdered his sandy hair or wore a wig. In his office he kept a tame mockingbird, uncaged, and callers were likely to find him padding about in his carpet slippers, whistling to the bird.

He was grateful for Dolley Madison's assistance with his

official entertaining; he continued to seek it. She was his hostess at any function to which ladies were invited. But in addition to these formal gatherings, he gave two large public levees each year, on New Year's Day and the Fourth of July, when he received his guests alone, shaking hands and genially conversing with all who came.

Some of his guests were from far-off places — and some were picturesque. One New Year's Day five Cherokee Indian chiefs with twenty of their tribesmen arrived, the chiefs resplendent in gilt-corded hats, stiff military jackets, doeskin pantaloons and moccasins, the tribesmen naked to the waist, their faces and bodies garishly painted. Jefferson was delighted with the Indians, so engrossed in conducting them to the refreshments table and heaping their plates with food that he seemed to forget the presence of the British ambassador and other pompous diplomats.

He liked to talk with Dolley and to share with her his optimistic vision of the capital's future. The city of Washington, he said, was destined to rival Paris in beauty; and he was elated when she replied that she, too, was sure of it. He loved trees and had planted a great many of them in the grounds of the President's House and along the streets and avenues.

"If I were a despot, I should inflict swift and terrible punishment on people who kill trees," he said. "Let me tell you a story, Dolley. Once, as a lad, I met a very old man who was planting a grove of oak saplings around his home. The old fellow was so intent on his chore that I asked why he did it. I remember his reply. 'Ah, I know I'll never live to see these oaks except as the little puny things they are now,' he said. 'But I have imagination, my boy, and in my mind's eye, I see the trees in all their towering glory.' That was a wise man, Dolley!"

"And it's a nice story," she said. "I'll remember it."

Dolley knew that many critical problems confronted Jefferson; she heard of them from James, who also worked to solve them. Jefferson disliked war, but he was not a pacifist, and this he demonstrated in his defiance of the Barbary pirates.

The rulers of the Barbary States in North Africa had long been in the habit of preying on the merchant ships of other nations that cruised past their shores. England and other European powers had paid a yearly tribute to these pirates, so that their ships might not be overhauled and plundered. During the administrations of Washington and John Adams, the United States had doled out great sums of money in tribute. Such payments, Jefferson said, were bribery and must be stopped! Accordingly, he sent a squadron of warships into the Mediterranean. He set up a blockade, and there were some short, sharp battles in which American sailors showed daring and courage. Though it would be a decade before all piracy was abolished in the North African waters, Jefferson forced the ruler of Tripoli to sign a treaty guaranteeing that United States vessels could sail the Tripolitan coast unmolested.

But Jefferson and Madison saw Napoleon's rapidly growing empire as a much greater menace to American safety.

The population of the United States was now almost twice what it had been at the time of the Revolution. The country was stretching westward, the new states of Kentucky and Tennessee had been admitted to the Union, the immense Northwest Territory organized and partially settled. The region lying beyond the borders of the United States, extending from the Mississippi River to the Rocky Mountains, and from New Orleans to the Canadian boundary, was called Louisiana and had been ceded by France to Spain in 1763. Spain had granted to the United

States the right to navigate the Mississippi, and to deposit cargoes at New Orleans — thus American pioneers in the West had an outlet for their commerce.

But in 1802 it was learned that Spain had secretly ceded Louisiana back to France. Jefferson instantly saw the change as an appalling danger. Spain had been a comparatively peaceful neighbor, but Napoleon Bonaparte would be a different kind of neighbor altogether. By shutting off the Mississippi at its mouth, Napoleon could block the entire western boundary of the United States. How could this stranglehold be averted? Frightened Westerners said angrily that their government should at once declare war on France. And Jefferson thought of war — though only as a last resort.

Robert Livingston was then the American minister in Paris. Early in 1803 Jefferson sent James Monroe as a special minister to aid Livingston. They were instructed to see whether France would sell New Orleans and west Florida to the United States. They met with Talleyrand, Napoleon's minister, who made a most astonishing counterproposal: Perhaps the United States would like to buy *all* of Louisiana?

Livingston and Monroe had not been commissioned to negotiate so vast a transaction, but they did not hesitate to seize this opportunity. For the price of fifteen million dollars, by a few strokes of a pen, the United States acquired the Mississippi River from source to mouth, and was suddenly increased in area from less than nine hundred thousand to more than one million, eight hundred thousand square miles.

News of the Louisiana Purchase reached Washington on July 3, the eve of Jefferson's annual Independence Day reception. A message came promptly from the President to James Madison.

"We have bought Louisiana at a bargain," Madison said to

Dolley. "Of course, the element of luck entered into it. I suppose Napoleon's motive for selling can only be guessed at. Well, he is essentially a conqueror, not a colonizer. His mad obsession is the total conquest of Europe; he may have thought that the time and effort needed to colonize Louisiana would hinder him in his frenzied grasping for power."

"And the payment in cash may have been an inducement," Dolley suggested.

"Yes, yes," Madison said. "Conquest is always an expensive game."

The Madisons went next day to the President's House. In the yard a band was playing patriotic music, the rooms were thronged and noisy, the punch bowl had been often drained and replenished.

"How pleased everybody is, Jemmy," Dolley said.

He smiled. "Not everybody, my dear. There will be people to denounce the Purchase as rash and reckless. The Federalists will probably say it's unconstitutional. I believe, though, that ultimately it will be viewed as a major achievement of Thomas Jefferson's administration."

In 1804, a young Englishman in Washington wrote in his journal: "I never saw prettier girls anywhere. As there are but few of them, however, in proportion to the great number of men, it is one of the most *marrying* cities on the whole continent."

Among the pretty girls were Anna and Mary Payne, ably chaperoned by their sister, the charming Mrs. Madison. Mary found her "superior" husband in Congressman John G. Jackson of Virginia. Anna had been courted by several ardent swains, and now was marrying Richard Cutts of Massachusetts, a youthful member of the House of Representatives.

Dolley liked Richard Cutts, she rejoiced in Anna's romance,

the spring wedding was held in F Street. James gave the bride away; the wedding breakfast was festive and toasts were drunk in sparkling champagne.

"But what shall I do without you, darling?" Dolley asked woefully, as Richard waited to lift Anna into his carriage.

"Anna, you're as truly our dear child as Payne is," said James.

She kissed them both. "This isn't good-by, it's just *au 'voir*. Richard and I will be back here before the snow flies, Dolley. And, James, I'll always be your dear child."

The Madisons were going to Montpellier for the summer. As Dolley busily shrouded the parlor in dust sheets, she was shocked to hear that Alexander Hamilton had been shot to death in a duel with Aaron Burr.

All of Washington, the country from end to end, was shocked. At the first garbled reports, people gasped incredulously; as verification came, there was an outburst of angry comment. Dueling was not illegal or unknown, but it had become uncommon in the East. The quarrel between Burr and Hamilton was not unknown, for it was of long standing — but who could have surmised that it would ever have this dire climax, the death of Hamilton, a man of such prominence and prestige, at the hands of the Vice-President of the United States?

The fact was that Burr had never forgotten the election of 1800, when he and Jefferson were tied for the Presidency, and Hamilton had persuaded his Federalist followers to vote for Jefferson. Burr had sulked over that, for the ambition to be President was a consuming flame in his breast. And more recently, he had wanted to be elected governor of New York, his native state — and Hamilton's. Once again, it was Hamilton who thwarted him.

In the heat of this campaign Hamilton **had** written abusive articles about Burr, which were published in the newspapers. Goaded and furious, Burr said that Hamilton must retract or meet him on the dueling field. Hamilton knew that a duel was no trifling thing; his own son, the oldest of his children, had been killed in a duel; but he was as vindictive as Burr was vain, and he would not retract. He accepted Burr's challenge.

They met at six o'clock of a July morning, on the dueling field at Weehawken, above the Hudson River. Only the two men who were their seconds watched as they paced off the ground, turned and faced each other in the gray-green light of the summer dawn, and leveled their pistols. It was said later that at the signal Hamilton raised his gun and fired into the air — while Burr took deliberate aim and shot to kill. Burr denied this; the seconds neither denied nor confirmed.

Hamilton fell, mortally wounded, and within twenty-four hours was dead.

Burr's behavior afterward was not that of a man who knows himself guilty of ruthlessness. The duel, he said, had been fair; he, rather than Hamilton, might have been killed. He was still Vice-President of the United States. He went back to Washington and when Congress reconvened, he presided over the Senate as calmly as though there had never been a breath of gossip about him. If some of his colleagues walked by him without so much as a nod, he seemed oblivious of it.

"You have heard, no doubt, of the terrible duel and death of poor Hamilton," Dolley said in a letter to Anna.

She was too discreet to say more than that. Perhaps when she saw Anna, they would talk of the duel, but even then she would guard her tongue, for she was never a gossip.

At Montpellier that summer, she thought often of Aaron Burr. She was loyal in her friendships, and Burr had been her friend, a friend of her family's. She remembered how he had spoken so gently to her about his daughter. Theodosia was a young woman now, married to Joseph Alston, a wealthy South Carolinian. Dolley thought of Theodosia and pitied her for the scandal that had involved her father.

"Poor Hamilton?" . . . But wasn't Aaron Burr just as unfortunate? The duel had been terrible indeed, a thing unwarranted by any civilized standards. Yet there was no proof that, as duels went, this one had been unfair.

"James," she said to Madison, "lacking proof, I cannot believe that Aaron Burr is a wicked man."

"No," said Madison quietly. "We must be unprejudiced and keep an open mind."

Thomas Jefferson was re-elected to the Presidency in 1804, with George Clinton of New York as the Vice-President. Dolley attended their inaugural; but she was suffering from what she described as a "bad knee," an affliction that grew worse and soon confined her to bed.

In July she rose and ventured out, hobbling painfully. Mr. Jefferson's granddaughter, Virginia Randolph, was to be married late that month.

"The President begs me to get Virginia's wedding garments," Dolley wrote to Anna, "also trinkets and dresses for all the family. I shall drive to the shops . . . am not able to alight, but I must do my best for them, and have promised to be at the wedding, if possible."

The shopping for the Randolphs was very interesting, but it was exhausting, too; and when the time came for Virginia's wedding, Dolley was so ill that Madison took her to Philadelphia, where she could be treated by the famous Dr. Physick.

"And here I am on my bed, Anna," she wrote, "with my dear husband sitting anxiously by me, who is my most willing nurse. But you know how delicate he is. I tremble for him."

Though Dolley may have trembled for James's health, he had no thought but for hers. For three months he sat anxiously by, seeing that she had every care and comfort.

At the end of October, Dolley insisted that he go back to Washington. The President needed him, she said. And Dr. Physick had assured her that she would be well in one more month. "You must go, James!"

So he went — and immediately she was wretchedly lonely for him. Reaching for her portfolio of writing material, she began a voluminous letter: "A few hours only have passed since you left me, my beloved, and I find nothing can relieve the oppression of my mind but speaking to you in this, the only way. . . ."

Madison replied warmly and tenderly. This was their first separation of any length in ten years of marriage. They bridged it in "the only way," with their daily letters.

As Dolley slowly convalesced, she had a stream of callers. Some were Quakers from the Pine Street congregation, and their reminiscences of the old days were not all soothing. She wrote to Anna that one Friend had "lectured" her, saying that she had too much company: "It brought to my mind, Anna, the time when our Society used to control me entirely, and debar me from so many advantages and pleasures. Even now, I feel my ancient terror revive to a great degree."

Madison sent the chariot, driven by Peter, his trusted coachman, to fetch Dolley home; and Anna and Richard Cutts came on from Massachusetts to travel with her.

"You look quite recovered, Dolley," Anna said. "Yes, and joyful."

"I am joyful at the thought of seeing James again," she said.

"Heavens, all those bandboxes and packages!" Anna exclaimed. "You can never cram them all into the chariot."

"Oh, yes." Dolley stacked the boxes and packages, and smiled at her sister. "There's ample space."

"But what's in them?"

"I had to do a bit of shopping, just a bit. The Philadelphia stores are so up to date, aren't they? I got some bonnets for Mrs. Randolph — she'll be with her father for the winter, and Mr. Jefferson was worried about her headgear, which often is not *quite* in the mode. And I got some presents for Payne. He's going off to school after Christmas. James says that Payne is old enough for boarding school." Dolley paused. "Oh, I hate to think of that, but of course James knows best."

"School will be good for Payne," said Anna.

Richard Cutts was peering at the horses. "A new pair, isn't it, Dolley? Very fine matched blacks."

"I bought them yesterday," she said. "A surprise for James."

Richard laughed. "Rather a costly item, I'd think."

"Yes, rather. But you know Jemmy. He *likes* fine horses." Dolley nodded briskly. "Well, let us start. I am all eagerness to be at home."

With Mrs. Randolph in the President's House, Dolley had fewer duties there that winter, but the Randolphs still sought her advice about their "garments," and she gave it — sometimes with unexpected results.

At a holiday ball, Mrs. Randolph turned to Anna Cutts, at her side. "Anna," she said, "*who* is the stylish-looking girl talking to Mr. Madison?"

"It's your daughter, Mrs. Randolph," Anna answered.

"Oh, no! It can't be — not in that *extremely* fashionable gown."

"The gown is one that Dolley bought for her."

"Dear *me!*" murmured Mrs. Randolph. "Surely Dolley must have the magic touch, Anna. She can transform geese to swans."

Aaron Burr's daughter, Theodosia Alston, spent the winter in Washington. Fearing that some people might be unkind to her, because of her father, Dolley made a friend of Mrs. Alston, and the two tall and elegant ladies were often seen together — Mrs. Madison always vivacious and buoyant; Mrs. Alston beautiful, but somewhat cool in manner.

"It's being said that Theodosia Alston is haughty," Anna told Dolley. "She seems disdainful."

"I think she assumes that manner to conceal a feeling of uncertainty and perhaps embarrassment," Dolley said. "I think she was very brave to come here, and we should be especially courteous to her."

As for Aaron Burr himself, he was in and out of the city. He dined once at the President's House; he escorted his daughter to dinner at the Madisons' in F Street. People wondered about him: they said he had no money at all. Though he was a lawyer by profession, he no longer had an office or clients anywhere, and seemed to have no further political ambitions.

In the spring Burr was said to be journeying through the West and the Southwest. He was popular in those rough regions. Dueling was not frowned on there: to have killed a man in a duel was not thought to be a very serious offense. Westerners were reckless and complaining nowadays; along the border of Mexico, they skirmished constantly with troops of the Spanish government. They said that their own government neglected them; President Jefferson was unconcerned about the welfare of American citizens in their section of the country. Many of them clamored for a war with Spain and western newspapers even hinted darkly that the West might secede from the Union unless it was given more protection.

Jefferson did not reply to the newspapers — but in November of 1806, he issued an abrupt proclamation. A conspiracy against the United States government had been discovered, said the proclamation. All citizens who might have become enmeshed in the conspiracy were warned to withdraw at once. The conspirators would be ferreted out and arrested, with their weapons, vessels and military equipment.

Aaron Burr was not named in the proclamation; but he was instantly suspected of being one of the conspirators. For where was Burr? Not in Washington. No, he had been absent for months. When last heard of, he was in the West. With the means of communication so scanty, the West seemed almost as remote as the moon; but strange tales of Burr had sifted back across the miles, vague rumors, contradictory and perhaps exaggerated, yet disturbing for all that.

A little later, and as suddenly, Jefferson ordered army officers in the Southwest to take measures against an expedition which was moving down the Mississippi River. General James Wilkinson, who commanded at New Orleans, was ordered to defend that city and port against a possible attack.

Soon afterward, down in Mississippi Territory, Aaron Burr was arrested by a detachment of United States soldiers as the leader of the mysterious conspiracy. This revelation was as stunning as a bombshell exploding. The nation rocked with it.

What was the purpose of the conspiracy?

For many months and from many sources, secret information had been forwarded to President Jefferson, tracing Burr's devious steps. Shortly after the duel with Hamilton, he had gone to the British minister in Washington and said that for half a million dollars he would start a revolution in the western states. When the British minister rejected the offer, he took it to Spanish agents who did not answer yes or no, but kept him dangling.

Then he toured the West by way of the rivers, the Mississippi, the Cumberland, the Ohio. Wherever there was any person, or group of persons, to listen to him, he proposed some sort of scheme — though seldom twice the same. He was enlisting recruits and the tale he told was the one which he thought most likely to appeal to that particular audience.

At times he said that, with British money and warships, he would establish in America an independent empire consisting of the western states, Louisiana, Florida and Mexico. Another version was that he planned to take possession of the West and Louisiana for Spain. Again he said that with Spanish aid he would capture the national capital and set up a dictatorship there. But to still other people he lied boldly and blatantly, saying that war between the United States and Spain was just about to be declared and President Jefferson had sent him into the West to prepare this area for the beginning of the war.

Having spread his net so wide, he caught several different kinds of citizens in it. At Marietta, Ohio, he recruited Harman Blennerhassett, a rich and foolish immigrant from Ireland, who lived in a great house on an island in the Ohio River. Entranced by Burr, Blennerhassett gave him large sums of money and agreed that the island should be the headquarters for Burr's men and a flotilla of boats.

But his chief conspirator from the start had been General James Wilkinson — and here he was dealing with a man who had no scruples or morals at all, an expert in treachery. While serving as a general in the United States Army, Wilkinson was also a paid spy of Spain, known to his fellow spies as "Number 13." As soon as Wilkinson saw that Burr's wanderings were being investigated and none of the schemes could be carried out, he hurriedly betrayed him by writing to Jefferson and disclosing everything — except his own villainy.

In December, with sixty men and ten boats, Burr had sailed from Blennerhassett Island for New Orleans, where he thought Wilkinson would join him. Floating down the Ohio, then down the Mississippi, he put in for supplies one morning at a little landing thirty miles above Natchez. It was there he learned that his arrest had been ordered. Abandoning his companions to their fate, he disguised himself, obtained a horse and fled toward Florida, expecting to find sanctuary among the Spanish villagers.

He rode hard through the wilderness, through a dark and rainy winter night and was not far from the border when he was overtaken and seized.

Burr was tried for treason in the House of Delegates at Richmond, Virginia, before John Marshall, Chief Justice of the United States. The trial was sensational, dragging on for weeks, the courtroom always densely crowded. Wilkinson was the principal witness against Burr; his testimony was a mixture of truth and lies. Others who testified were just as confusing, for nobody seemed to know exactly what had been Burr's intentions — perhaps he did not know himself. The lawyers argued long and furiously; the question of whether or not Aaron Burr was a traitor somehow got lost in a thicket of legal technicalities, and at last he was acquitted.

But most people believed that he was a traitor, and there were those who said that it would have been better if he had fallen in the duel with Hamilton. Though Burr maintained his calm, even insolent, bearing, he knew that he was an object of scorn to his countrymen. From Richmond he went to Baltimore, then to Philadelphia, finally to Europe.

In the investigation of the Burr conspiracy, President Jefferson had counseled with Madison. After the arrest was made, Dolley had written to Anna: "I suppose you have heard that

Burr is on his way to Richmond for trial." Dolley did not go to the trial, and she never talked about it. There had been too much talk, she thought. The decision of the court would stand; now wagging tongues should be silenced.

Her own life was going on much as usual. Washington was like a kaleidoscope; each season brought new people into the circle of political society which seemed more and more to revolve around herself. As Anna once had said, she was wholly devoid of conceit, and she could not think that what she did was important — yet she realized that it might have some value. These people whom she drew together, either in her own house or as Jefferson's hostess, varied in their politics but were all striving toward an ideal. Perhaps by making them feel at ease with one another, she helped to promote harmony and mutual respect where discord and hatred might otherwise have flourished.

"And I enjoy doing it," she said to herself. "I suppose it's just my natural bent."

Henry Clay, the young Senator from Kentucky, was among the newcomers to the capital. Clay knew James Madison and went to call on him in F Street. Dolley was in the kitchen, baking a cake that morning; Madison was in his study; the maid Sukey was cleaning the upstairs rooms. When the knocker clattered, Dolley slid the cake pan into the oven, rolled down the sleeves of her gingham house dress and hastened to the front door.

Senator Clay smiled at the flushed and pretty young woman who opened the door. Her cap was askew and she had a smudge of flour on her cheek.

The Senator lifted his hat. "Is Mr. Madison at home?" he asked.

Dolley saw instantly that she was being mistaken for a servant. She stifled the impulse to giggle and nodded with downcast eyes. "Yes, sir. Will you please to step in, sir?"

He stepped in and with typical Kentucky gallantry he kissed her.

Madison also had heard the knocker. At this moment he walked into the hall.

"Jemmy," Dolley said, turning to link her arm through his. "Jemmy darling, a caller."

Senator Clay gasped. "Why, you are Mrs. Madison!" But he was equal to the occasion. Bowing, he added: "Ah, had I known that, madam, the coin would have been larger!"

Dolley laughed. She was amused, and she did not mind that the story got about and amused other people, for it was never repeated maliciously. She liked Senator Clay. They became good friends.

Sometimes he teased her gently. "Everybody loves Mrs. Madison," he said.

Her response was always quick and spirited: "And Mrs. Madison loves everybody."

12

FIRST LADY

Months before the expiration of Jefferson's second term as President, it was known that he would not run again, and that he wanted James Madison to succeed him. The two men had always seen eye to eye; as Secretary of State, Madison had played an active role in mapping the course of government. The Republican party was strong; the Federalists had never rallied from the blow of Alexander Hamilton's death. In 1808 Madison was nominated and then elected.

As Dolley watched the tide of politics that swept her husband into the Presidency, she was more sorry than glad. She still thought of that office as the most exalted in the world; but she had been too close to it not to know what a strenuous and thankless task it was. She knew that however efficient a public official may be, there are always people to find fault with him. She knew her husband's goodness and dreaded to think that anyone would ever speak ill of him. She felt that he would be happier at Montpellier than in Washington, and his happiness meant more to her than anything else.

When friends congratulated her on Madison's election, she said with a rueful smile: "I don't know that there's much cause for congratulation. Do you see the iron gate at the front of the President's House? And the weeping willow trees at the side? The President of the United States may come in at the iron gate — and go out at the weeping willows."

Jefferson had no such doubts. He was elated by the election results. He had complete confidence in the "great little Madison." These were perilous times. Napoleon had made himself Emperor of France and was warring with England. Both of these European powers seemed hostile to the United States; England had never ceased her annoying persecutions of Americans on the high seas. Jefferson had preserved the peace; he knew that Madison would make every effort to preserve it, too.

"What man can do, Mr. Madison will do," Jefferson said stoutly.

James Madison was inaugurated in the newly built House of Representatives. His face was pale as he recited the oath. In his suit of brown woolen cloth ("American cloth!" said observers approvingly) he looked small and slender, but his blue eyes were clear and steady, and his voice was resolute.

After the ceremony a reception was held at the F Street house, and in the evening there was a very grand inauguration ball at Long's Hotel. Dolley's old friend, Captain Tingey, had suggested the ball, and she had consented to it. The Madisons would not dance, she said, but for the young people it would be pleasurable.

Captain Tingey garlanded the hotel ballroom with flowers, and draped it with flags and bunting. The night was chilly, so the Captain had fires kindled in the fireplaces at both ends of the dance floor. The guests came early, hordes of them, pushing in, laughing and chattering. The orchestra had composed special music for this event; behind a screen of ferns the fiddlers tuned their instruments and waited for the arrival of the honor guests.

At nine o'clock, and at a gesture from Captain Tingey, the orchestra struck up with "Jefferson's March," and Mr. Jefferson strode into the ballroom with Mrs. Madison on his arm. Dolley's gown was of buff-colored velvet with a long train; her turban ("from Paris!" whispered the ladies, enraptured) was of the same velvet, trimmed with bird of paradise feathers. Her only jewelry was the string of pearls that James had given to her to mark this memorable date.

Then the music changed to "Madison's March," and in came the new President, escorting Anna Cutts. Anna looked beautiful, as always, and radiant because James had chosen her to be his partner.

More guests crowded in; the ballroom was so full and overheated that Dolley asked Captain Tingey to have a window opened. But the windows were nailed shut, no amount of tugging would budge them! A nervous lady moaned that she was fainting. A nimble gentleman took off the lady's slipper, vaulted to a window sill and smashed the glass with the slipper heel. A current of fresh air flowed in, the lady revived, the gentleman jumped down from the sill, restored the slipper to her foot and bowed complacently. Dolley smiled her gratitude, and the dancing began and continued until dawn.

At midnight, at the supper table, President Madison had Anna on his right and Mrs. Robert Smith, the wife of the new

Secretary of State, on his left. Mrs. Smith was chagrined that she did not have the right-hand chair; she felt that it was her due and she pouted. But there were few to condone with Mrs. Smith, for Anna Cutts was a favorite in Washington, second only to Dolley herself.

Across from the President, Dolley was seated between the British and the French ministers, and it was noted that she behaved as amiably to the one as to the other.

"She is so tactful," people murmured. "Mrs. Madison is the soul of tact."

Thomas Jefferson went back to Monticello, taking with him his servants and his furniture, and the Madisons moved into the President's House. Dolley was not surprised to find that their furnishings from F Street were inadequate for these many enormous rooms — and she had an idea. Why should this house be stripped to the bone and then refurnished every time a new Presidential family came into it? How much more sensible and practical, she said, if it could have its own *permanent* things and be maintained always in a livable condition!

To her delight, Congress considered the idea and saw the wisdom of it. Funds were appropriated and Benjamin Henry Latrobe was appointed to superintend the work.

Latrobe was an architect of taste and ability. He had helped to design the Capitol and other government buildings, and he had definite notions as to what was required of him now. But he knew that Mrs. Madison had a real talent for homemaking, and he was quite willing to consult with her.

They agreed that the great drawing room should be decorated in yellow, with curtains, cushions and wall coverings of satin or damask. Latrobe went to Philadelphia and bought mirrors and lamps for this room. In Baltimore he bought sofas, mantel-pieces, andirons and chairs — and, at Dolley's urgent request, a fine piano and a guitar.

"Mr. Latrobe, you have attained a very artistic effect," she told him, when the drawing room was complete.

"Artistic, indeed," he said, "and you have contributed to the effect, madam."

They quarreled mildly about the hanging of the Gilbert Stuart portrait of George Washington. Dolley liked the portrait; she thought it was extraordinarily good and should have the most conspicuous place in the house.

"Above the drawing room mantel, Mr. Latrobe," she said.

He frowned. "The dining room is properly the picture room, Mrs. Madison. I have just the proper spot in mind for George Washington."

"But, Mr. Latrobe — "

"The dining room," he said firmly.

"Of course, if you *insist* — "

"I do, madam."

Dolley laughed and gracefully assented, and the portrait was hung where Mr. Latrobe wanted it.

The Madisons would need a steward now, someone to manage the details of housekeeping and the other servants. For this post they employed Jean Pierre Souisatt, a native of Paris, who had been the British minister's butler in Washington. "French John" was a big, black-browed man, very correct in manner and efficient at his duties.

With the house in readiness, Dolley planned her season's entertaining: a levee every Wednesday afternoon through the autumn, winter and spring, some "evening drawing rooms" and several large formal dinners. She sent out no invitations for the levees, which were announced in the *National Intelligencer*, Washington's newspaper, as open to the public. For her first levee Dolley lighted the house with a thousand candles and engaged the Marine Band to present a concert. Beautifully dressed and glowingly cordial, she greeted all who came, while beside her Madison smiled, shook hands and made the little bobbing bow that was his habit.

The "evenings" and dinners were smaller affairs, though Dolley was careful to invite to them not only Madison's Republican friends, but also his Federalist opponents. "For James is their President, too," she said. "Republican or Federalist, we're all Americans, one people, aren't we? So long as I'm a tenant here, this house will not limit its welcome to the members of any one political group."

Her parties were never stilted. The refreshments were bountiful and delicious, and she saw to it that her guests were never bored. Often there was music, sometimes she brought in her parrot and had the comic bird speak and sing for the company.

One night a gentleman guest said to her: "Mrs. Madison, you are carrying a book. In fact, at these functions you seem always to have a book with you. I think you must be extremely fond of reading."

"Oh, my book?" Laughing, she held it up, a vellum-bound copy of *Don Quixote*. "Do you know I've never read a word of it! I wish I had the time for reading. In my old age, I shall read — but not now. No, the book is merely a social asset, like my snuffbox, a means of starting conversation with people who may feel bashful here. 'Have you read *Don Quixote?*' I say to such a person. 'Won't you have a pinch of snuff?' He is obliged to reply, either yea or nay — thus the ice is broken and soon we're well acquainted."

Dolley's concern was always for the bashful guests, on them she bestowed her kindest attention. Once at a large reception she saw a young man standing stiffly in a corner, his back flattened against the wall, his face crimson with embarrassment, a cup and saucer clutched in his shaking fingers. As she watched, he raised the cup to his lips and gulped down the coffee it contained, but the saucer slid from his grasp and fell to the floor. In an agony of shyness, he looked around; then, wild eyed, he stuffed the empty cup into his coat pocket.

Poor young man! Dolley remembered his name and that he was from Philadelphia. She walked toward him. "I believe I knew your mother years ago," she said.

"Did — did you?" he stammered. "I — I dropped the saucer. Rather, it fell, it just *fell* — "

"Someone bumped into you, probably. In a crowd like this one can't avoid being jostled. I'll see that the servant brings you more coffee. Tell me, how is your mother?"

The young man obeyed. He told Mrs. Madison about his mother; and, as she listened, smiling, he felt less and less embarrassed. At last he took the cup from his pocket and held it out to her. "I guess you saw me hiding it, ma'am."

"Yes. I think that in the circumstances, I should have done the very same thing."

"Thank you," he said earnestly. "I'm glad I came to your party today. I've had a good time, Mrs. Madison."

The levees, the receptions large and small, the little intimate dinners that Madison gave for the men in his cabinet, the afternoon "Dove Parties" to which only the wives of Congressmen and diplomats were invited — all of them Dolley fitted into her calendar. Nor did she slight the children.

Somewhere she had heard that in ancient Egypt, the children of the Pharaohs had gathered on a certain day each year to roll colored eggs at the base of the Pyramids. A children's fete! Why not have something like that now, in America, in Washington? In the Easter season, which was approaching, and for all the boys and girls in the city?

She sent French John to the market to buy eggs, hundreds of eggs. She hardboiled the eggs and painted them red, green, blue, purple. Then, through the newspapers, she invited the children of Washington to an egg-rolling party on the lawn behind the President's House on Easter Monday.

The children came — and what fun it was!

"A custom in the Egypt of the Pharaohs," Dolley said. "Who knows that it may not become a custom *here?*"

To people who knew her only casually, Dolley might seem always blithe and gay, but her emotions were deep and sincere, and she was never blind to the realities of life. She was unswervingly loyal to her relatives, her family. Once she had written to Madison: "My darling husband, to find that you love me, have my child safe, and that my mother is well, comprises all my happiness." Now as the months went by, and talk of war spread insidiously, she worried constantly about James, the heavy burdens under which he labored, the tension in the country.

And she worried about Payne.

He was a tall, dark, fine-looking youth, almost a man. To herself Dolley acknowledged that Payne was also a problem. He had not done well in the boarding school to which Madison sent him, or studied seriously at home with a tutor. Madison wanted

him to have a college education, but there seemed little likelihood of his ever passing the examinations which would admit
him to any college or university.

He was clever at sports, cut a dashing figure on horseback,
danced beautifully and had a winning smile, but was wasteful
with his money, fond of gambling and often drank more than
was good for him. He was polite to Dolley and his stepfather,
but seldom deferred to their wishes and seemed utterly indif-
ferent to the affection they lavished upon him.

What was wrong? she wondered. Had Payne been too much
petted? Lucy Washington said so. Too much coddled, Lucy said.
Perhaps it was true, Dolley thought. Perhaps she had tried to
make up for her own sternly restrained childhood by showering
Payne with the things she could never have, and so had missed
Lucy's middle path between a rational firmness and overindulgence.

But if an error had been made, it wasn't Payne's and he must
not be blamed for it. No, the error was hers. And now it seemed
that she could only love her son, and pray that someday, somehow, she might have a more satisfactory relationship with him.

In these years Madison was endeavoring to stave off war with
England, absorbed in a situation that was increasingly grave,
though not new to him. As Secretary of State, he had seen each
shift of the wind, the old grievances flaring, subsiding for a
while, flaring again. England connived with the Indians in the
American Northwest, meddled with American commerce, impressed American sailors. Jefferson had been patient with such
incidents; Madison was just as patient, his heart crying out for
peace. But now Congress was dominated by a clique of young
Senators and Representatives from southern and western states
where the war feeling ran high.

The younger legislators, known as the "War Hawks," were hot for conflict. Their slogan was "Tree Trade and Sailors' Rights"; they shouted it raucously, without surcease, drowning all voices of caution. And at length they prevailed. In June, 1812, the war with England was declared.

It was a war that never had the endorsement of the whole country. The conservative New England states branded it as unnecessary, a setback to prosperity, a war the nation was poorly prepared to fight. The Federalists said that it was "Mr. Madison's War."

13

WAR!

The Federalists were bitter and sarcastic when Madison was re-elected in 1812. Besides charging him with having caused the war, they said it was his wife for whom the electors had voted: it was Dolley, not James, whom the people liked.

"Mrs. Madison is boss in that household," they said. "Petticoat rule!"

Madison's friends retorted angrily to these jibes. "Petticoat rule? Nothing could be farther from the fact! Mrs. Madison would never attempt it — and if she did, Jemmy would not for a minute put up with it!"

Perhaps only Dolley knew how his country's danger weighed upon James Madison, and upon herself, too, for she was still Quaker enough to believe that any war is a futility and an evil. And this one, as it developed, seemed strange, slow, discouraging. Even those Congressmen who had so loudly demanded it were sobered, beginning to speculate about what it might accomplish.

On land there had been dreary reverses to American efforts. The regular army of the United States, never big, had dwindled in recent years. Many of its officers were old men who had fought in the Revolution; they seemed to be awkward and blundering now. Volunteers were scarce, and the Federalist governors of several eastern states refused to call out their militiamen to swell the ranks of the regulars.

The War Hawks had shouted that the American forces should conquer Canada, but this was easier said than done. The British in Canada had the Indians as their allies. Expeditions sent against them were repulsed on three fronts and ended dismally, with Detroit in British possession, the garrison at Fort Dearborn massacred, and the buildings burned to the ground.

In the early months of the war, Americans had good news only from their navy — a raw little navy of sixteen vessels setting forth to contend with what was thought to be the most powerful of all navies. For years England had boasted of her mastery of the seas. Yet within a short time, the American ship *Constitution* had triumphed over the British frigate *Guerierre*, the American sloop *Wasp* captured the British *Frolic*, England's mighty *Macedonia* became the rich prize of the frigate *United States*, and the reconditioned *Constitution* demolished the big British frigate *Java*.

Americans were astonished and gleeful at the skill and valor of their navy. England, just as astonished but irate, retaliated by blockading American ports. Boldly, American privateers proceeded to attack British merchant ships, confiscating more than three hundred of them.

Then on September 10, 1813, Captain Oliver Hazard Perry with a fleet of nine vessels challenged the British on Lake Erie and by brilliant tactics scored a smashing victory. Perry's terse dispatch reporting the battle electrified his countrymen: "We have met the enemy and they are ours; two ships, two brigs, one schooner and one sloop."

But did such successful engagements mean that the war would soon be over? James Madison thought not.

"All this while England has been involved in a European war with Napoleon," he explained to Dolley. "England hasn't concentrated on her struggle with us — and won't, until Napoleon is overthrown. We shall feel the effect, when that occurs."

In April, 1814, Napoleon abdicated his throne in defeat — and very soon fourteen thousand British soldiers, veterans of the Duke of Wellington's invincible army, were sent across the Atlantic to invade the United States at three points: Lake Champlain, New Orleans and Chesapeake Bay.

In August, General Robert Ross with four thousand of those veterans disembarked at Benedict, Maryland, a town at the mouth of the Patuxent River, and marched north toward Washington. Ross had been ordered to destroy the American capital and to seize President Madison and his Cabinet members. Behind Ross's regiments, anchored in Chesapeake Bay, were twenty-seven British ships commanded by Rear Admiral Sir George Cockburn, and primed to bombard villages and terrain along the coast.

Jovial and swaggering, Commander Cockburn had said to General Ross that the hospitality of Mrs. James Madison was quite famous. "I shall avail myself of it," he said, "I'll make my bow at her drawing room."

"And I will dine at her table," said General Ross.

More than once during the war it had been rumored that the British might march on Washington, but the possibility had hitherto seemed remote. Now a courier galloped to the President's House to say that they were actually on the road, nearing the boundary of the District of Columbia.

Madison listened grimly to the courier, knowing that little had been done to defend the city. John Armstrong, his Secretary of War, and General William Winder of the Army had squabbled about it, each man believing it was the other's job. As a result, the project had bogged down in red tape and neglect.

"But the city must be defended, Dolley!" Madison said. They were at breakfast. He pushed away his plate, rose and strode the length of the room, his brow furrowed. "Winder is at Bladensburg now, that's right on the District line. I'll go to him. We have some militiamen in the neighborhood. They must be rounded up to make a stand. We must try to stop Ross in his tracks."

"Why should the British wish to destroy Washington?" Dolley asked.

"Not for any military advantage," Madison said. "Destruction for the sake of destruction! Vandalism. We raided towns in Canada — as we should not have done, I never favored it. This is their revenge."

"You will not go alone to Bladensburg, James?"

"No, some of the Cabinet will accompany me."

"And you think Ross can be stopped?"

"I don't know," he said. "But I shall not be captured! No, nor will you! Colonel Carroll and a hundred men will guard the house. Wait for me here. I'll keep in contact with you — and I'll come back." He paused. "If the worst should happen, I want you to try to save my papers. They are in four cases in my office upstairs."

Dolley's heart was racing. The papers were precious. At the time of the Constitutional Convention, long ago, Madison had recorded the sessions of the convention. No one else had done so. If Madison's papers should be lost, there would be no notes of the sort anywhere, nothing to show future generations of Americans how their government came to exist.

"If I send you word to leave the house, will you see that the cases are removed and deposited in the Bank of Maryland, Dolley?" Madison asked.

"Yes, I will," she said.

He lifted her hand and kissed it. "Are you afraid, my dear?"

"Not for myself. Only for you, James. Please be careful!"

"Oh, yes. Remember, wait here until I come — or until I send some direct warning. Really, I can't believe it will be necessary!" He turned to speak to French John Souisatt, who was at the door. "Well, John?"

"Your coach, sir. And this bulletin has just come."

Madison read the bulletin and sighed. "Our Commodore Barney has blown up his gunboats in Chesapeake Bay."

"Oh, James!"

"It was either that — or surrender to Cockburn. I must go now, Dolley."

She walked with him to the coach, watched as he stepped into it — a slender, black-clothed figure, smiling at her, then whisked quickly away.

"Madame," said French John, "will the President be at home for dinner tonight?"

"I think so, John. Yes, and probably he will bring several gentlemen. They'll be tired and hungry, wanting a good meal. Please see to it."

But was this what she thought?

She went to her bedroom. For once there were no guests, no one was in the house except herself and the servants. She sat at an open window and looked out at the street.

It was noon, the August day very hot. The street, the whole city, seemed ominously still.

A clock on the bureau ticked off the hours, the sun shone fiercely, the odd stillness held. Then people appeared in the street, some on foot, more in chaises, carts, wagons — a welter of traffic. A lady came to the President's House: Mrs. Smith, whose husband was editor of the *National Intelligencer*. Mrs. Smith said that an alarm had been issued from the *Intelligencer* office. All the able-bodied men in Washington were told to hasten to Bladensburg to join the defense companies; all women and children were advised to leave town immediately.

"So that's what it is, Mrs. Smith?" Dolley gestured toward the window. "An exodus. Seeing those people, I was reminded of the fever epidemic in Philadelphia. This time the flight is from war, not disease. I think war is even more terrible."

"Mrs. Madison, you must leave, too," said Mrs. Smith.

"I can't. I have no conveyance."

"I have. Let me take you with me."

"No," Dolley said. "The President asked me to wait here. Thank you, I must stay."

At dusk she received two pencil-scrawled communications from Madison. Neither told her where he was; but in one he said he now feared the worst, the other warned her that the enemy was stronger than had been reported and she must be prepared to quit the house at an instant's notice.

She summoned French John and inquired whether he had seen any indication that the British might be advancing on Washington.

"No, madame," John said. "Not yet, though the city is crawling with their spies. A ragged fellow was in the yard this afternoon. A spy, pretending to be a beggar, whining for food. His rags did not fool me. I sent him kiting."

"Please fetch my trunks from the storeroom, John, and the four cases from the President's office. And get me a carriage."

"A carriage, Mrs. Madison?"

"A vehicle. A wagon, a dray, the kind doesn't matter, just so it has wheels and a team of horses hitched to it."

"There seems to be a shortage of vehicles, but if one is available you shall have it, madame." John wrinkled his black brows thoughtfully. "You know, do you not, that Colonel Carroll has withdrawn his soldiers from the premises?"

"What!" She had not known this. "The house is not guarded at all? I am sure that Mr. Madison believed Colonel Carroll would not leave."

"The Colonel has gone," John said. "And the servants are badly frightened. They talk of slipping off to the woods."

"Tell the servants they have my permission to do so. Not for the world would I have any of them harmed."

"Well, I shall not go, madame. And Sukey says she wants to stay with you."

"I shall be glad for Sukey's companionship. Let her remain, and the others go."

"Yes, Mrs. Madison." John hesitated. "There is one thing more, a little inspiration of mine."

"An inspiration?"

"We have the cannon at the gate. If you allow me, I spike

the cannon and lay a train of powder. If the redcoat rascals come, I light the fuse, the powder ignites, flashes. *Pouf! Bang!* We see that they are all wafted high as the heavens, and fall to earth in tiny shreds."

"Oh, you can't, John!" Dolley exclaimed.

"Your pardon, madame, but I can. It is a simple thing."

"It's outrageous — savage! No, no!"

"Mrs. Madison, this is war. But, as you say — " he shrugged and bowed. "I am obedient to your wish."

Night descended, dark and stifling hot; the noises in the street faded, it was quiet again. John fetched the trunks, the cases. With Sukey's help, Dolley neatly packed Madison's precious papers into the trunks, packed also some of the most valuable of the Presidential silver plate, the pair of eagles which were the President's insignia of office.

"I see many things of my own I'd like to rescue," she said to Sukey. "Of course, I can do without them."

Sukey's starched calico skirts rustled as she bent to lock the trunks. She looked up. "Mrs. Madison, aren't you forgetting your parrot?"

"Oh, the parrot! How dreadful of me, Sukey."

"Don't you fret, Mrs. Madison," Sukey said, smiling. "In the morning I'll get somebody to take the parrot. You ought to rest now, ma'am."

But how could she rest? She had never felt less like resting! She began to write a letter to Lucy.

"Dear Sister . . ." She wrote three paragraphs and thrust the page aside.

She put on a dressing gown and, with a candle in her hand, went downstairs, through the big silent house. In the dining room, by the flickering candle ray she saw the Stuart portrait of George Washington on the wall. The painted face seemed to question her.

"I should have made space in the trunks for the portrait," she said to herself. "It is a treasure. Perhaps I can fit it in even yet. Of course, Ross and Cockburn may not come. I don't know that they will. They may have been stopped at Bladensburg — somewhere. James may have stopped them."

Roaming from room to room, she thought of James. Was he in danger tonight? If so, she wished that she could share that danger! When he said that he feared the worst, did he mean he might be captured? The President of the United States a prisoner of the British? For a man of James Madison's sensitiveness, nothing could be worse! He would resist it to the last!

In the hall a shadow stirred among the darker shadows. Dolley shivered and the candle flame dipped.

"Mrs. Madison," a soft voice said.

"Oh, it's you, Sukey."

"Mrs. Madison, honey, you ought to go to sleep now."

"I supposed *you* were asleep, Sukey, hours ago."

"No, ma'am. But the clock's struck twelve, roosters'll soon be crowing. I've brewed you a nice cup of tea and set it on the table by your bed. Some biscuits, too. You didn't eat a morsel at dinnertime. Give me the candle, Mrs. Madison; I'll lead the way."

"Thank you," Dolley said meekly.

She handed the candle to Sukey, and they went up the stairs together.

14

INVASION

Dolley wakened at dawn to a hot and breathless morning.

She dressed and got a telescope from her desk drawer, went to the window and peered out. She saw far down the street a straggling group of soldiers in blue uniforms. As she watched, they dispersed and passed from sight. She went to other windows, leveling the glass. She saw some pedestrians, but no more men in blue, and no redcoats.

Well, perhaps this inactivity was all for the best. She would resume her letter to Lucy.

She wrote slowly — no, really she hadn't the heart for it! She was too anxious about James. And in the distance were muffled sounds that might be the roar of guns.

At noon Sukey brought her a light luncheon. Sukey said that she had found somebody to care for the parrot.

"Good! And has John procured a wagon?"

"One is promised him," Sukey said. "He's gone now to fetch it."

At three o'clock two dust-covered couriers came to tell Dolley that a battle had been fought at Bladensburg.

"A battle?" she said. "So I did hear guns!"

"To be truthful, it was a rout, Mrs. Madison." The couriers shrugged and looked remorseful. "We had militia troops. They were green as grass — and scared. The British blasted at us and we retreated."

"Did you see the President?" she queried. "The Cabinet members?"

"Yes, Mrs. Madison. They were on horseback, they got away before Ross could nab them."

"Was the President unhurt?"

"Yes. We saw him riding toward Georgetown."

"Then he may be here soon," Dolley said. "I'll wait for him."

The couriers looked dubious. "The British are over the District line. Five hours at the most and they'll be in the city. You would do well to go immediately, Mrs. Madison."

"Did the President bid you tell me that?"

"No," said the couriers. "We didn't talk with him."

"Then I must wait a little longer," Dolley said.

Sukey took the couriers to the kitchen and gave them food. French John hurried in.

"I have the wagon, madam," he said. "It is very shabby and not large."

"The trunks are not large," Dolley said. "Fetch a ladder, John."

"A ladder, Mrs. Madison?"

"We'll save the Washington portrait," she said.

John stared incredulously, but went out, returning in a moment with a ladder on his shoulder. In the dining room Dolley steadied the ladder and John mounted it. The portrait was screwed tightly to the wall. As John sweated and worked at the stubborn screws, the front door slammed, someone dashed through the hall to the dining room door.

It was Colonel Carroll.

"Mrs. Madison!" the Colonel panted. "I've come for you — "

"I thought you had deserted me, sir," she said coolly.

"No, no! A contradiction in my orders, I can explain it. But not now! I come from the President, to get you out of this house at once — "

"My husband sent you?"

"Yes. I'm to conduct you to the home of a Mrs. Minor in the Virginia woods. Mrs. Minor is the wife of an army officer — "

"I know Mrs. Minor, sir, and when John has the portrait down I'll go with you."

"Portrait! My dear lady, you're in peril of your life! Portrait!"

"It must not be abandoned to the British," she said. "Think what a flourish they would make of Washington's portrait! Do the screws stick, John? Break the frame and give me the canvas."

As Colonel Carroll fussed and fumed, John doubled his fist, broke the portrait's gilt frame and loosed the canvas.

"There, it is done." Dolley neatly rolled up the canvas. "Now, John, get the trunks into the wagon."

"Trunks! Really, Mrs. Madison!" cried the irate Colonel.

She brushed by him and went out to the wagon. At that moment a carriage careened from the street, into the yard. Two men leaped out. Dolley knew the men; they were Robert de Peyster of Westport, Connecticut, and Jacob Barker of New Orleans, two friends of James's.

"Mrs. Madison, we heard you were still here," Jacob Barker said. "What can we do for you?"

"You've come just in time, gentlemen," she said. "James wants these trunks deposited in the Bank of Maryland. I didn't quite see how I was to get them there. If you could — "

"Certainly, certainly!"

Mr. Barker helped John to heave the trunks to the luggage rack of the carriage. Mr. de Peyster strapped them down.

"And this canvas," Dolley said. "It's a painting."

"Ah, yes. To the Bank of Maryland, Mrs. Madison. And what about you?" Mr. Barker asked. "Will you not ride with us?"

"No, sir. I go with Colonel Carroll — at the President's orders."

The laden carriage whirled again toward the street. Sukey scurried around for a few last parcels to throw into the wagon; French John got up to the driver's seat and shook the reins.

"Mrs. Madison!" Colonel Carroll shouted angrily.

She had darted into the house to scribble an end to her letter to Lucy.

". . . And now, dear sister, I must leave this house. . . . When I shall see or write you, or where I shall be tomorrow, I cannot tell! " . . .

By three-thirty they were at the edge of the city, Colonel Carroll riding his horse ahead, John driving, Dolley and Sukey in the bed of the wagon.

Scarcely half an hour afterward, Madison with two aides galloped into Washington by another road, halted at the President's House and swung from their saddles.

Madison ran into the hall. "Dolley!" he called. "Dolley!"

There was no response, his voice echoed hollowly through all the empty rooms.

"My wife has gone with Carroll," he said to his aides. "I had hoped to reach her before the Colonel arrived. It would have reassured her and I myself could have conducted her to Mrs. Minor's."

The wagon crept at a snail's pace, for the road was choked with weary militiamen retreating from the rout at Bladensburg. The sun sank; it was night — and no night ever darker, Dolley thought. She was tired, miserably uncomfortable, and she knew they were still many miles from the concealing depths of the Virginia woods.

"But the papers and the portrait are safe," she said to Sukey, "and that's a great deal to be thankful for."

At eight o'clock they saw rows of tents, an encampment of American soldiers. Colonel Carroll dismounted and spoke to a sentry, then stepped to the wagon.

"We'll have to spend the night here, Mrs. Madison; if we went on, we might miss our way. This man tells me that you and your maid can have a tent; John and I can bunk somewhere."

Dolley and Sukey got stiffly out of the wagon. The tent to which they were ushered contained two burlap cots. They sat on the cots and supper was brought to them — soldier's fare, beans and bread, a mug of coffee.

It was very hot inside the tent; Sukey said they wouldn't sleep a wink. But when they had eaten, they lay down on their cots; sheer exhaustion engulfed them and they slept.

Next morning they started forward, crossed the Potomac River by ferry, jogged on in dust and smothering heat. The day was cloudy, the air humid and close. At noon the little procession halted at the home of Mrs. Love, a patriotic lady, who gave the fugitives an ample meal and wished them luck on their journey.

The clouds thickened as they went on again; a wind was rising, a shrill, whistling wind that whipped dust into their eyes and blanketed their clothes with dust and grit. Thunder growled and lightning flashed.

"It's going to storm," Sukey said.

French John glanced back at the two women. "More like a hurricane blowing up," he said. "This is no common wind."

Colonel Carroll was pointing toward a building in a lane that angled off from the road. The Colonel shouted something, but his words were not distinguishable in the gale's tumult. John slapped the reins, urging the horses to a trot.

Then the clouds seemed to split wide; rain crashed down in torrents, in sheets, a deluge of rain, blinding and impenetrable. The horses stumbled and plodded through water and mud.

Dolley and Sukey crouched on the flooded floor of the wagon, drenched to the skin, seeing nothing, hearing nothing. Beneath them the wheels slithered, jerked sharply, then stopped.

They were in the yard of the building to which Colonel Carroll had beckoned them — a tavern, by the look of it. John jumped to the ground, got Dolley and Sukey out of the wagon and propelled them through the pelting rain to the tavern porch. He told them to go in, while he and the Colonel stabled the horses.

Hand-in-hand they entered what seemed to be a sort of anteroom, or vestibule, very clean, with a stairway going upward. There was nobody in the vestibule.

"Hello!" Dolley said, but she got no answer.

Behind the stairs was a small door that she thought might lead into the tavern taproom. She knocked and waited.

"Someone must be here, Sukey," she said. "There's a smell of cooking."

Sukey sniffed. "Soup, Mrs. Madison. A kettle of soup. It smells good."

"Perhaps the lady of the house is upstairs. We must find her."

They started up the stairs just as the small door was flung open. Dolley looked over the stair rail at a woman who stood there. The woman wore an apron and a cap, her face was a furious red and her eyes glittered.

"Mrs. Madison!"

"Yes?" Dolley said.

"Ah, I recognize you, Mrs. Madison. I'd have recognized you anywhere. I didn't need the military gentleman to tell me — that wet and muddy gentleman, bursting into my scrubbed kitchen — "

"The gentleman is Colonel Carroll," Dolley said. "I'm sorry he muddied your kitchen. He will apologize. We were caught in the storm — "

"Get out!" the woman said. "Out of my house!"

Dolley gasped. "If you please — "

"Mrs. Madison, my husband is a soldier. He is fighting the war *your* husband made. Mr. Madison's War!"

"Oh, no! No — "

"I'll not have Mr. Madison's wife under my roof!" The woman's voice soared to a shriek. *"Out with you!"*

Dolley felt her heart pounding, surging with resentment. She wanted to tell this hysterical woman how fine James Madison was, how the war distressed and harrowed him. But she only said, quietly: "Very well. Come, Sukey."

So they went out again and the wind tore at them and the sky was lightning-streaked above them. A clump of lilac bushes offered a little shelter, they huddled into it.

"You s'pose the rain'll ever slack, ma'am?" Sukey asked.

"Oh, yes," Dolley said. "I think it's tapering off now."

By evening the wind was down, the rain had slacked to a drizzle. Once more the wagon took to the road, toiling through the Virginia forest, into a clearing, past some tilled fields, at length to Mrs. Minor's farmhouse. Someone was on the veranda.

"James!" Dolley cried. "Oh, James, I am so relieved!"

Madison drew her with him into the house. Mrs. Minor got her some dry clothing, a supper of bread and meat, a soothing pot of tea.

"You poor dear," murmured Mrs. Minor. "Such adventures!"

Alone with James, Dolley told him how she had disposed of the trunks.

"It was just the right thing," he said. "If anyone can get the papers through to Maryland, Barker and De Peyster will do so. When I found you were not in Washington, I came here to wait for you. You know that the city was burned?"

"Was it, James? How dreadful!"

"I'm not sure as to the extent of the damage. The reports I've had are very confused. I think that private property was mostly spared, but the public buildings were destroyed."

"The President's House — "

Madison shook his head. "I don't know. I was on the far side of the Potomac. I could see the flames. The fire was still raging this morning. Except for the rain, it might be raging yet! That downpour was our salvation."

"Will the British occupy the city?" Dolley asked.

"Probably not. They have nothing to gain by an occupation. I daresay they're now marching toward the Patuxent to board their transports. I shall know tomorrow when I go back to Washington."

"James, you must not be captured!"

He smiled. "My dear, I'm rather determined not to be. I have a squad of troopers with me and feel that I'm out of harm's way — for a while, at any rate."

But at midnight a hard-riding messenger roused Mrs. Minor's household to say that bands of raiders were pursuing the President, combing the countryside, searching all farms and residences. Madison hastily conferred with Colonel Carroll.

"It may be a false alarm — or it may not," he said to Dolley. "I think Carroll and I had better leave at once."

"You must have the troopers to guard you, James."

"A few. The others will patrol here."

There was no time to say more. He kissed Dolley and soon was clattering off in the dark and misting rain.

At daybreak she talked with John Souisatt. She said that she had decided not to stay on at Mrs. Minor's. If the raiders were in the vicinity and searching all houses, they would search this one, too. She had been recognized by the woman at the tavern as the President's wife; she might be recognized again.

"You could disguise yourself, madame," John suggested.

"I mean to," she said. "Even so, I can't remain here and perhaps bring disaster on Mrs. Minor, who has been most kind. I shall start back toward the city, John."

"I'll harness the wagon. Have you told Sukey, madame?"

"No. It would be better if I traveled without you and Sukey. The tavern woman may have given the raiders a description of the three of us, and the wagon. No, I'll borrow a farm cart from Mrs. Minor."

John protested. "Mrs. Madison, you should have a man with you!"

"I'll take two of the soldiers. We'll be farm people, going to market. Tomorrow, if all seems well, you and Sukey can follow in the wagon."

John did not like the plan. "But I know that you will do whatever you think is wisest, madame — "

"Yes," she said.

Mrs. Minor provided Dolley with a muslin print dress, a shapeless coat and rusty black bonnet. The two soldiers donned the blue denim garments of farm hands and concealed their weapons under a pile of straw in the bottom of the cart. At eight o'clock they set forth, jogging through the woods and then along the roads. The morning sparkled; the world looked as if yesterday's torrents had scoured and polished it. No marauders and only a few other travelers were to be seen.

In midafternoon they reached the Potomac ferry. The boat was beached on the near riverbank; the ferryman was seated in the grass and weeds at the water's edge. One of the soldiers hailed him and he got to his feet.

"Can't put you across today," he said. "General Winder's orders. Big ruckus over in Washington last night, enormous big fire. Nobody's to come into the city, General Winder says, only army officers, maybe, or folks connected with the gover'ment. Ferry service suspended till further orders."

Dolley leaned from the cart. "Is General Winder in Washington? Then the British have gone?"

"Yes, ma'am," the man said. "Scooted. It was the storm that did for them. When the hurricane struck, they took to their heels like a bunch of perishing rats."

"Is President Madison with General Winder?"

"The President, ma'am? Now that I couldn't tell you." The man grinned broadly. "I don't see a lot of our Jemmy here lately. Not a whole lot. Reckon he's busy, and so am I."

"You must take me on the ferry," Dolley said. "I'm Mrs. Madison — and on my way home."

The man glanced at her coat and bonnet. "Jemmy's wife? From what folks say, she's a mighty fine and stylish lady."

"I really am Mrs. Madison — "

He laughed. "Reckon I've got eyes in my head, ma'am. You can't josh me."

"Look!" said the soldier roughly. "This *is* Mrs. Madison, and you'll do as she wishes without more fiddle-faddle."

The man grunted, blinked and then was convinced. The cart was driven onto the boat and the boat shoved into the river's current. As they crossed, he spoke of the invasion, the buildings which had been destroyed, the Capitol, the Treasury, the Congressional Library, the Arsenal —

"The President's House?" Dolley said.

"Oh, yes, ma'am. It was one of the first to go."

"Are you positive?"

"Only the walls are standing today, ma'am."

Fifty sailors and marines had set fire to the house, tramping into the yard, each man with a long pole to which was fixed a blazing oil-soaked torch. At a command from Admiral Cockburn, the windows were splintered, the torches tossed in.

"Cockburn and Ross had inspected the house earlier," the ferryman continued. "Nosing around, impudent-like, bragging. Seems they'd vowed they'd eat dinner there — well, they did sit down in the dining room and drink a bottle of wine, the scoundrels! Cockburn picked up an old hat of Mr. Madison's and some pretty yellow sofa cushions and carried them off as souvenirs. Anyhow, that's what I've heard, ma'am."

Dolley thought sorrowfully of the stately rooms, the damask and draperies, the piano and guitar — the yellow sofa cushions!

She thought of Mr. Latrobe and of Mr. Jefferson, of all the people, thousands of them, whom the house had welcomed, to whom it had been a symbol of their country's enduring strength. And now only the walls standing, a gray stone skeleton, scarred and derelict!

The boat snubbed the pier; the cart rattled up the cobbled slope and into the city. The streets were littered with ashes and soot, mired with the hurricane's debris. Smoke and the odor of scorched timbers hung, thick and acrid, in the air.

Dolley asked the soldiers to drive her to F Street, where Anna Cutts lived, in the house that had formerly been the Madisons'. She wondered whether her sister would be there? Indeed, would the house still be there?

But the fire had not hurt F Street, and Anna was at home.

"Oh, Dolley!" she cried, hugging her, weeping over her. "My darling Dolley!"

"Do you know where James is, Anna?"

"Yes, don't you? Why, James is in Washington," Anna said. "He came this morning. He's had scouts out looking for you, Dolley. How *enraptured* he'll be to see you!"

The reunion of the fugitives in Anna's parlor that evening was a happy interlude, but the ensuing weeks were arduous. Though Anna begged them to stay with her, James felt that as President he must have an official residence. Octagon House, the large and luxurious home of Benjamin Tayloe, had not been destroyed and the Tayloes were at their summer home in the mountains. James rented Octagon House, and the Madisons installed themselves — "and *just* ourselves," Dolley said, "for we have no traps or gear!" Soon they learned that the trunks and the portrait were in good hands. Then French John and Sukey returned, John got together the staff of servants, and life assumed a somewhat normal aspect.

Madison at once reorganized the government, naming James Monroe as the new Secretary of War. Many citizens felt that the city had been wrecked beyond repair, it might be expedient to seek another site for the national capital and begin to build all over again. But Madison said *no* — very emphatically. This site, marked out by George Washington, was the proper place for the capital; already history, tradition and sentiment had hallowed it. Of course the city could be rebuilt, he asserted. And when the war was won, it would be!

With the same firmness he said: "We will win the war."

He had previously sent commissioners to Europe to discuss a peace with representatives of England. The delegations met at Ghent, in Belgium, the Czar of Russia acting as mediator. England was tired of the war; her ministers were coming slowly to realize that she could neither reclaim nor dominate the colonies lost to her by the Revolution. Those colonies were now forged in the bonds of a proud young nation that never again would be subject to any foreign power. But England was proud, too, and obstinate. If there was to be peace, England wanted to dictate the terms.

While the discussions dragged on at Ghent, month after month, the fighting went forward — a bit more hopefully now for the American forces, as if the shameful burning of Washington spurred them to desperate courage.

In September the British fleet sailed from the Potomac, up Chesapeake Bay, into the Patapsco River to attack Baltimore and then to bombard Fort McHenry. All day the British cannon boomed and hammered at Fort McHenry, but the defenses held fast, undaunted. All day and all night the American flag flew gallantly above the ramparts — and in the morning was still flying. Witnesses watched and marveled as the British were repulsed; and one of them, a Baltimore lawyer named Francis Scott Key, seized pen and paper and wrote four eloquent verses that, set to music, would become a national anthem, the *Star-Spangled Banner.*

The next onslaught of the enemy was at New Orleans, January 8, 1815, a short, fierce battle with startling results. In thirty minutes, the intrepid General Andrew Jackson of Tennessee, commanding five thousand sharp-shooting western militiamen, cut down Sir Edward Pakenham's attacking army of seventy-five hundred, the very flower of England's veteran regiments. The British retreated, dazed and crushed, their losses in that tumultuous half-hour numbering two thousand and thirty-six. Of Jackson's men only eight were killed and thirteen wounded.

Though it was not known, not even surmised, at the time, the Battle of New Orleans occurred two weeks after articles of peace had been signed at Ghent. On February 11, a ship bringing the peace treaty docked in the harbor of New York. Rumors of its arrival spread quickly to Washington. On February 14 the treaty was delivered to President Madison.

"Peace!" The city celebrated madly, joyously. Dolley lighted Octagon House from attic to cellar and held a vast impromptu levee. People flocked to the house, eddied in and out, surrounded it, cheering, laughing, dancing in the street.

Closeted in an upper room, Madison and Monroe gravely studied the Treaty of Ghent.

It was not a good treaty; it was a makeshift. England had not admitted that she was anywhere at fault, had not conceded the justice of the American cause — had conceded almost nothing.

But Madison and Monroe knew that the Battle of New Orleans had effectively concluded this War of 1812, and in a way the British were not likely to forget. The United States had established their independence for all time to come. Henceforth, the two nations would exist, not as perpetual foes, but in dignity and mutual respect, as comrades.

15

THE BLESSINGS OF PEACE

The end of the war brought with it a period which would be known in American history as the "Era of Good Feeling." More than ever before, American citizens were confident of their government's future and united in their interests. Even the disputes of party politics seemed to decrease. James Madison was suddenly seen as a truly great President, and what had been "Mr. Madison's War" was now "Mr. Madison's Peace."

For Dolley this was not a time of idleness. The Madisons were obliged to give up Octagon House to its owners and to move to much less elegant quarters in a row of houses called the Seven Buildings. Their small house here had no fence or yard; its front wall was flush with the pavement, passers-by could look right in at the windows.

"And they do!" Dolley said. "I suppose they think that I won't mind it."

In fact, she liked it. The faces looking in were all friendly and smiling. Her parrot cage was at one of the windows; every day schoolchildren congregated in the street to see her feed the parrot. Opening the window, she would greet the children and coax the bird to perform his tricks for them.

The army was being disbanded now, regiments of soldiers were trudging through the city. Somehow they all knew which house was the President's and would halt for a moment to shout: "Hurrah for Mrs. Madison! *Hurrah!*" Then Dolley would run to stand in the doorway and wave her handkerchief. "Godspeed!" she cried. "God bless you and guide you safely home!"

The medium-sized rooms in the Seven Buildings were rather inconvenient for entertaining, but Dolley's hospitality had not diminished, and she gave many dinners, teas and receptions, using the limited space to its best advantage. These gatherings she called "squeezes," explaining that the word had been coined by her sister Lucy, and she thought it singularly appropriate. To the "squeezes" came friends and acquaintances, new and old, strangers, the public. Henry Clay's comment was often quoted in Washington: "Everybody loves Mrs. Madison."

The largest and most important of the "squeezes" was to honor General Jackson, who visited the capital in the early summer of 1815. To Tennesseans Andrew Jackson had always been a hero, the "strong man" of his state, soldier, lawyer, member of Congress, Senator, Judge of the state supreme court; his dramatic victory at New Orleans had made him the hero of the nation.

The people of Washington had heard innumerable tales about this famed "Sharp Knife" of the West, Old Hickory, the Indian fighter. They crowded to the windows of the little house in the Seven Buildings, clamoring for a glimpse of him. What would they see? A rugged frontiersman, uncouth and long haired, in buckskin?

Peering in, they saw a tall, thin man, straight as a ramrod, with keen blue eyes in a tanned, hawklike countenance, wearing his gold-braided uniform with an easy grace, and manners that combined modesty and a sort of old-fashioned chivalry.

"Andy Jackson will be President sometime," the people said. "But not next time" — for it was known that, though Madison would not again be a candidate, both Madison and Thomas Jefferson were favoring the candidacy of James Monroe, and that Jackson, too, would support Monroe.

In the autumn of 1816, Monroe was elected. On January 1, 1817, Dolley was hostess to the usual big New Year's levee — her last, as the President's wife. She made the occasion very gay, something that her guests would never forget, with especially good refreshments, beautiful decorations and a, program of music. Her rose satin gown was trimmed with ermine, gold chains encircled her waist and arms; her white satin turban was topped with ostrich plumes and a crescent of brilliants.

Madison was retiring to his plantation, as George Washington and Thomas Jefferson had done at the close of their administrations.

"Yes, we go soon to Montpellier," Dolley said, as she shook hands all around. "I truly believe it is the happiest kind of life."

At Monroe's inaugural ball on March 4, she was resplendent in yellow velvet. Friends clustered about her, expressing regret that she should be leaving them. It seemed incredible, they said; she had been a vital part of the capital scene, without her nothing would be the same.

Elizabeth Collins Lee was in Washington that night, but illness in her family kept her from the ball. She sent Dolley a letter:

"... Eight years ago, I wrote you to congratulate you on the joyful event that placed you in the highest station our country can bestow. I then enjoyed the proudest feelings — that my friend, the friend of my youth, who never had forsaken me, should be thus distinguished and so peculiarly fitted for it. How much greater cause have I to congratulate you now for having filled it as to deserve the gratitude and thanks of the community. . . ."

Dolley cherished that letter.

"Dear Eliza!" she said. "As if I could ever forsake her!"

Anxiety for her son Payne somewhat clouded Dolley's last weeks in Washington. At Madison's suggestion, Payne had gone to Ghent with the peace commissioners — and his conduct there had been puzzling and displeasing to his stepfather. The men on the commission, Henry Clay, John Quincy Adams, Albert Gallatin, knew Payne Todd and liked him, but were not sure what services to require of him. His time had been mostly his own, and he spent it hilariously in a roistering jaunt over the continent of Europe.

Payne had been treated as royalty by the Europeans he encountered. To them, the President of the United States was a ruler, ranking with kings and emperors: therefore, this young man, as the President's son, must be a prince.

And Payne himself hadn't said that he was not a prince. No, never! Let them think it. So much the better! All the snobbish affectations that were so odious to James and Dolley Madison attracted Payne. Posing romantically, he had squired the titled ladies about, flirted with a countess, danced with the Czar of Russia's sister.

He had seldom written to Dolley, and then only to ask for money. She knew that Madison regularly sent him generous amounts; she wondered why he should need more — but she did not refuse him. She never guessed that he was borrowing from Richard Cutts to pay his gambling debts. Now that he had come back to her, she wanted him to marry and settle down. In the hope that he would do so, she had introduced him to the prettiest girls in Washington — to no purpose, for he seemed to have no thought of marriage.

"I believe Montpellier may be good for Payne," she said to Anna. "The simple life of the plantation may make him more serious."

"Perhaps it will," said Anna.

Now that he had retired, Madison could take up again his plans for the remodeling of Montpellier. His father was dead, his mother growing very old and feeble. He added wings to the house, designing one of them as a separate dwelling for his mother.

"She has been the mistress here for years," Dolley had said, "and she will be happier if she still can have her own domain, her servants and familiar furnishings. We must be careful that your mother never feels she has been superseded, James, or has become a pensioner."

When the wings were in place, Madison built a portico at the side of the house and a long pillared gallery across the front. Then he improved and expanded Dolley's garden.

Many people were eager to help with the Montpellier garden,

bringing seeds and cuttings of rare flowers and shrubs. Neighbors contributed rosebushes, friends abroad sent orange trees from Spain and clumps of heather from Scotland. Thomas Jefferson came often from Monticello to see how the tiger lilies, the Cape jasmine and oleanders were progressing, for Jefferson was an authority on gardening, as on a hundred other arts and sciences.

It grieved Dolley to know that the years were dealing harshly with Mr. Jefferson. Though never a rich man, he had been prosperous — now he was in financial difficulties. Openhanded and liberal always, he had given away much of his fortune, or had used it to defray his expenses as a public official. Some of it had gone for the education of his daughter Martha's children, the twelve young Randolphs, and more to the maintaining of Monticello as a haven — almost a hotel — for a constant influx of visitors. The profits from his farming had not balanced his expenditures; the crops he harvested were scanty and fetched low prices. He had sold pieces of his land. He had sold his magnificent library to the government — where it would be the basis of a new and modern Library of Congress.

Actually Thomas Jefferson was on the verge of poverty. But he had one last dream! — the founding of a great school at Charlottesville. This University of Virginia would be his last work for his native state; he was devoting himself to it now, heart and soul.

It seemed to be the custom that visitors who arrived at Monticello, and stayed there for weeks, months, perhaps a year, would then drive on a few miles farther to stay as long at Montpellier.

"Yesterday we had ninety persons to dine with us at one table," Dolley wrote to Lucy Washington. "The dinner, on the lawn, under the arbor, was profuse and handsome."

Visitors, multitudes and cavalcades of visitors, from every corner of the United States, from foreign countries! Never had Dolley been required to entertain on so grand a scale, so "profusely." She felt that it was all very flattering, that anybody who trod a path to the Madisons' door paid them a compliment — and yet sometimes she was weary.

"We have had more company this summer than I can enumerate," she said in a letter to Anna. "This morning I was not able to breakfast with my eighty guests. I went for a ride with my dear husband."

Madison also liked company. Seated at his dinner table, he was at his best, a clever and witty conversationalist. As one appreciative lady commented: "Every sentence he speaks is worthy of being written down." But as season followed season, he realized, as had Jefferson, that company could severely strain a man's purse.

He and Jefferson were in strangely similar circumstances, and Madison perceived their dangers. It was not uncommon for the Montpellier tobacco crop to be disappointing, or even to fail entirely, while the cost of feeding and clothing his slaves seemed always greater. He brooded about slavery: the institution was not only morally wrong, it was impractical! He believed that the whole plantation system in the South was doomed. He foresaw that someday there would be a crisis, something drastic done, the system abolished.

He knew that he was living beyond his means. How, though, could he retrench? Not by barring his door to visitors, that was not to be thought of! Not by skimping his allowance to Payne; he had a father's love for Payne. But he feared for Dolley, who was seventeen years his junior and would certainly outlive him.

Madison's most fervent wish, overshadowing all others, was to provide for Dolley.

In 1821 he began to collect his state papers, so that they might later be published. His notes of the Constitutional Convention were a chronicle of a nation's birth, each stage recorded as it occurred. Other men had made scattered notes, but no one so accurately, in such detail. His writings were unique; when published, they would be immensely valuable. He could imagine that in the distant future (or perhaps not so distant!) Montpellier might have to be sold, either in fragments or all of it. The Madison papers, sorted, copied and in order for the press, would then be his real legacy to the wife he adored.

His first idea was that Payne should act as his secretary in this task, but Payne was often and mysteriously absent from home, not at any time to be counted on.

"Can't I do the copying, James?" Dolley asked.

He smiled. "Would you like to?"

"Yes. And you know my brother Temple once said that I write a fine, clear hand."

"An excellent hand," said Madison. "And in every sense the papers are yours. But for you, they might have been reduced to ashes."

Dolley's days then had a kind of pattern. She was up early of mornings, dressed quickly, and for an hour rode horseback with James along Montpellier's wooded lanes. Or if the weather was too bad for this exercise, they walked briskly on the gallery — sometimes, if nobody was looking, they ran foot races, though only at a moderate speed, and with much laughter and joking. From ten to three in the afternoons they worked, Madison sorting and editing the sheets of his manuscript, Dolley copying them. From three o'clock until nightfall, Dolley could see to her housekeeping and the entertainment of her guests.

By comparison with the busy months of spring, summer and autumn, the plantation winters were quiet and restful. A dozen people might stay on through the winter, but they were mostly relatives, cousins, nephews and nieces — "homefolks," as Dolley said, "so nice and no trouble." The house was cozy and warm, log fires glowing in every room, fragrant bouquets brought in from the conservatory, the music boxes playing tinkling tunes. Dolley had whole hours together of delicious freedom, in which to write letters to Lucy and Anna, or to read the pamphlets and books that came with each week's mail.

She read the novels of James Fenimore Cooper and Sir Walter Scott — and now she read her vellum-bound social asset, *Don Quixote!*

16

SUNSHINE AND SHADOWS

The years, Dolley thought, were like one of the piece-quilts on her linen cupboard shelves — checkered with patches, some bright, some somber.

In 1824 John Quincy Adams, the son of John Adams, was elected to the Presidency, and the Marquis de Lafayette arrived in America to be present at the dedication of a monument commemorating the Battle of Bunker Hill.

Both men were old friends of the Madisons'. John Quincy Adams had long been associated with James in governmental affairs; Dolley had known him when he was a young Congressman in Washington and she had frequently stopped her chariot and taken him up the steep climb to the Capitol building. Lafayette was just at the start of what would be a triumphal tour of the country for which he had fought so bravely in the Revolution. Congress had voted a gift of two hundred thousand dollars and a township of Florida land to the Marquis. He would travel over most of the United States; but first he came with his large party of fellow tourists to stay briefly at Monticello, and for several weeks at Montpellier. This was indeed a compliment, Dolley thought, and she exerted herself to make the visit a happy one.

In 1826, on July 4, Thomas Jefferson died at Monticello. He had experienced the joy of seeing the University of Virginia opening its doors to students — and then died a bankrupt. For this great American there was no wonderful gift from Congress. Shortly before his death, the sum of sixteen thousand, five hundred dollars had been raised by popular subscription — too little and too late to relieve his distress. His household possessions were immediately sold at auction. The next year, the entire Monticello estate was sold, except for a small plot of ground around his grave.

Madison's mother was in failing health. Dolley waited upon her constantly and tenderly. "Now I have become the child and you are my parent," the old lady often said. "Such a good parent!" In 1829, at the age of ninety-eight, she died and was buried in the Montpellier cemetery. After the funeral James and Dolley went to Richmond, where James was a delegate to the Virginia Constitutional Convention.

"A stimulating journey," Dolley wrote to her sisters. "I was excited to observe the city, the shops and street lights, for since the autumn of 1817, I had not been once away from the plantation."

And yet Richmond, too, had its shadows, reminding the Madisons of Aaron Burr's treachery and trial.

In 1830, in Philadelphia, Payne Todd was arrested and thrown into jail for debt. Payne communicated the news of this

catastrophe to Richard Cutts, who hastened to pay his debt and
the fine, and to secure his release.

"Oh, Richard, how terrible if Dolley knew!" Anna said. "She
must never hear of it. Never!"

But the story could not be suppressed; it reached Montpellier.
Horrified and bewildered, Dolley believed that there must be
some mistake. She sent money to Payne and frantically begged
him to come home. When he did so, she believed that he had
learned a lesson and would reform.

"Forgive my boy for his eccentricities, Anna," she said. "His
heart is all right."

"Yes, yes," Anna replied vaguely, and in a less hopeful tone.

And very soon Payne was off again, shunning Philadelphia
where he had been disgraced, but amusing himself riotously
elsewhere.

Dolley's many nieces and nephews loved her dearly. As if to
make up for Payne's "eccentricities," they were fondly attentive
to her. Lucy's children and Anna's sons corresponded with their
Aunt Dolley, confided in her, visited her at every opportunity —
and Annie Payne asked if she could not live with her.

Annie was the daughter of John Payne, Dolley's youngest
brother. John had been a farmer in Virginia, now he was moving his family to Kentucky.

"But I don't want to go to Kentucky, Aunt Dolley!" Annie
said. "I should miss you so! I want to stay here. Speak to Father
for me."

Dolley spoke to her brother. "Let Annie stay with me, Johnnie. For a year or two, anyway. She's a sweet, industrious,
intelligent girl. I should feel that for a little while she was
mine — the daughter I've always yearned for and never had."

John thought about it, and said good-naturedly that he had no objections. "You and Annie arrange it between you, Dolley." The arrangement, promptly made, was to be a lasting one, a source of never-ending comfort to them both.

In these years Madison suffered from rheumatism. He never complained, though the illness grew steadily worse, crippling his legs. Even when he could no longer walk, he was cheerful and serene. Wrapped in a black silk gown, a gray knitted cap on his head, a shawl over his thin shoulders, he lay on his bed or on the drawing room sofa and worked at his papers. The material for one volume was ready for publication; he kept the manuscript in a small red morocco trunk on his bureau. He told Dolley that this manuscript must be offered to Congress and that Congress would certainly purchase it. He was busily editing the notes for several more volumes.

He said that he was in an optimistic mood about the government because Andrew Jackson had been elected as President in 1836 and then re-elected. He had a very high opinion of Old Hickory's abilities. Many statesmen still came to Montpellier to consult with him; he was always delighted to see them.

"Accept my apologies for not getting up to greet you, and pull your chair near to me," he said, a glint of humor in his blue eyes. "Strange as it may seem, I talk better when I *lie*."

His voice was strong, his smiling patience unfaltering. The rheumatism crept into his hands; he had to wear woolen gloves and could not hold a pen in his fingers. Meals were served to him by his valet, Paul Jennings, but Dolley was at his bedside, day and night. She did all his writing now, read to him, conversed quietly with him or was silent, just as he wished. Their companionship had never been more complete and affectionate.

He died peacefully, in a moment, one morning in June, 1836.

Perhaps he had known that death was close — but to Dolley their parting seemed shockingly abrupt, and grief overwhelmed her.

In her loss, she had the sympathy of the nation. President Jackson sent her the resolutions passed by Congress in tribute to James Madison, and with them a personal letter of condolence. Relatives and intimate friends rushed to Montpellier to help her through this time of sorrow, and loving messages from young and old, the humble and the great, poured in upon her.

During the winter she offered the papers in the red morocco trunk to the government. Her attitude toward them was not quite what Madison's had been. She felt it was her sacred duty to see that they were published — not for any financial benefit to herself, but as evidence of her husband's patriotism, his lifetime of labor for his country. She explained this viewpoint to President Jackson, and he said that he fully understood it. On Jackson's vigorous recommendation, Congress bought the manuscript for thirty thousand dollars.

Dolley was encouraged, as if she were redeeming a pledge to James. She began to copy the material for the other volumes, writing fast, at fever pitch, allowing nothing to interfere. And then, suddenly, she was terribly tired and sad, and knew that she must get away from Montpellier, that only in different surroundings could she recover her spirits and the will to go on living.

She talked with Annie Payne. It was summer again, they strolled in the garden, talking. Dolley said that she hadn't much money. Half the payment from Congress had been given as an endowment to the University of Virginia. "James wanted that done," she said, and she added that she had recently paid various debts of Payne's — somehow it seemed impossible to prevent Payne from running into debt!

"But James owned a small house in Washington, Annie. The house is on Lafayette Square, it hasn't been sold. I think we must go there — perhaps just temporarily, until I'm rested. Payne assures me that he can manage the plantation and the crops better than I ever could. Well, this will be his chance to prove it. We'll leave everything here in his charge. The responsibility may be good for him, just what he needs."

Annie agreed. "You love Washington, don't you, Aunt Dolley? When did you last see it?"

"Twenty years ago!" she answered. "Oh, I suppose it will have changed out of all recognition. Of course the *world* has changed, Annie. Now we have steamcars on the railroads, steamboats on the rivers, steamships crossing the Atlantic! And the amazing inventions — why Mr. Samuel F. B. Morse is experimenting with the *telegraph* and declaring he can perfect it! And a man in Cincinnati has actually made a trip in a *balloon!*"

17

OLD FRIENDS AND NEW

In the autumn of 1837 Dolley and Annie Payne went to the house on Lafayette Square in Washington.

Yes, the city had changed! — Dolley saw that at a glance. There were new streets, blocks of flats, a park, hotels and stores. Jefferson's trees on the avenues had grown from saplings to a majestic girth and height. The President's House, rebuilt, with the original gray stone exterior painted white, was known as the White House; in it lived Martin Van Buren, the newly elected bachelor President.

It was a fine, enterprising city, Dolley thought. Probably as Mr. Jefferson had foreseen, it would eventually rival Paris in beauty.

"James was right to insist that the capital be retained in this location, Annie," she said. "And yet I feel like a stranger here. People have forgotten me. I can't think of a single person who might call on me."

John Quincy Adams was her first caller. Adams was now a Representative from Massachusetts. He had been chosen to announce Madison's death to Congress. He wanted to tell Dolley about his speech on that solemn occasion, and to extend his respects to her.

The next day Elizabeth Collins Lee called.

"Oh, Eliza, my treasured friend!" Dolley cried. "Is it really *you?*"

"It is," Elizabeth said, "and we're going to be boon companions again."

Then John Souisatt came, knocking at the door. Since the war, French John had been employed in a Washington bank, he had acquired a wife and family of children.

"Madame!" he exclaimed, with a sweeping bow. "How can I serve you? Command me. Anything!"

She smiled. "You are kind, John, but I lack for nothing."

"Do you plan to have a cow in the city, Mrs. Madison?"

"A cow?" she repeated, startled. "No."

"So you will lack for fresh milk and cream! Many city dwellers have cows — and the riddle of how to pasture them. You, madame, would have no difficulty at all. Behind my cottage on the outskirts of town is a stretch of green pasture. I suggest that you buy a cow, which I shall tend for you. Better still, let me act as your agent and purchase the animal, for doubtless I can drive a shrewder bargain. What do you say to this scheme, madame?"

She said, "Thank you, John. You may buy the cow and tend it for me. I shall like having plenty of fresh milk and cream."

Then, somehow, everybody seemed to know that she was back in Washington, and to come calling. It was almost as if the capital had been anticipating her return, keeping a place for her, a place that belonged only to Dolley Madison. Congress granted her the franking privilege and a seat in the House of Representatives — not in the spectators' balcony, but on the floor, with the legislators, an honor never before conferred upon a woman. She was invited to all official functions and frequently squired by President Van Buren himself.

On New Year's Day, to her astonishment, the throng that went to the White House levee drifted later to Lafayette Square and into her little double parlor. On the Fourth of July it came again — and this time she was prepared. Sukey and Paul Jennings, the two servants she had brought from Montpellier, were ready with wine and fruit cake, cookies, tarts and that wonderful confection *ice cream.* Soon Mrs. Madison's informal New Year's and July Fourth receptions were a tradition in the capital, just as Dolley once more, and without effort, had become a prominent and well-loved public figure.

She did not set the fashions now. She couldn't afford new clothes, but wore her old ones, unearthing from box and cedar chest the trailing velvets and brocades, the beads and sequins and towering, feathered turbans. Nobody would have thought of smiling at these elaborate, outmoded costumes, for they were worn with an air of modest dignity. It seemed to be generally understood that Mrs. Madison was a great lady, there was not another like her anywhere and she must be treated with a special courtesy.

In 1841, William Henry Harrison was inaugurated as President, died within the month and was succeeded by John Tyler, who had been the Vice-President. Mr. Tyler's wife was an invalid; the social burdens of the White House fell upon his daughter-in-law, Mrs. Robert Tyler. Young Mrs. Tyler was timid and inexperienced; she sought Dolley's counsel.

"Dear Mrs. Madison, the very notion of being the President's hostess frightens me," she said. "Won't you help me?"

"Of course, I will," Dolley said. "With pleasure."

Thereafter, it was no uncommon thing for Mrs. Tyler to dispatch the President's carriage to Lafayette Square with an urgent appeal: "Do come! I am in a dilemma." Laughing, Dolley would comply, remembering times in the past when, with Sukey, she had flown to Mr. Jefferson's rescue.

She went with Mrs. Tyler to the Capitol one day in 1844, to see Samuel F. B. Morse's first demonstration of the electric telegraph. Wires had been strung connecting Washington with Baltimore. The audience was large — and mostly skeptical, listening nervously for the message that might, or might not, be transmitted from the operator in Baltimore.

Click-clack-click. Miraculously words were spelled out: *What hath God wrought?*

Mr. Morse beamed. His invention had been perfected. This was his moment of supreme triumph. Turning, he looked around the tensely silent room for just the proper person to dictate the answering message.

"You, Mrs. Madison," he said.

"Nor was it in the least surprising that Mr. Morse should have asked you," Mrs. Tyler said later to Dolley. "Of all the distinguished people present, you were the most distinguished."

Distinguished, perhaps — and certainly hard up, Dolley thought ruefully. Congress hadn't yet purchased the second lot of James's papers. There had been obstacles, postponements;

with every year of delay, she was a bit poorer. And for herself, she did not mind. She felt that finally the sale would be completed. Meanwhile she could practice the strictest economy and make light of it. But she had Payne to cope with — and he was unwilling to economize in anything. When Payne needed money, and this was constantly, he reproached her because she had so little to give him.

"It's ridiculous," he grumbled. "It's shameful!"

She was desperately worried about Payne, a secret worry she dared not confess even to Annie, though the chill of it was always in her heart. His debts were an incessant drain upon her slender resources, and she was afraid not to pay them, for she was haunted by the memory of his arrest and imprisonment in Philadelphia — the one thing she could not have borne again!

She knew that he ignored his responsibilities at Montpellier. He seldom wrote to her, never responded to her letters, scarcely ever came to Washington to see her. But every summer she visited the plantation, finding it woefully neglected, the crops unharvested in the fields, the buildings going to wrack and ruin. From the servants she learned that Payne was often "sick," would "disappear" for long periods and then reappear, sullen and disheveled. She knew that he gambled; she suspected that he was drinking heavily.

"I fear Payne hasn't the training for farming, or the inclination either," she said to Annie, attempting to excuse him. "His talents are of another sort."

She sold some tracts of the Montpellier land, and then reluctantly sold the entire estate to Mr. Henry W. Moncure of Richmond.

"I couldn't have done it if Mr. Moncure hadn't also bought

the slaves and promised that none of them will ever have to leave the plantation," she said. "Montpellier is their home. I could never have consented to their being separated from it, parceled out, flung to the four winds. Mr. Moncure will care for them, as James did."

She had thought that by disposing of Montpellier her situation would be eased; but she was reckoning without Payne. Soon she discovered that he had used her credit to borrow a vast sum of money which he sank in a fantastic and worthless investment of his own. This debt was so large that it swallowed up what she had obtained from Mr. Moncure, and she had even to mortgage her Lafayette Square house to meet it.

And now she was extremely poor, facing destitution. She tried valiantly to conceal the fact, but her friends were aware of it. Senator Daniel Webster, who was both friend and neighbor, proposed to certain men in official circles that they establish a fund for Mrs. Madison, from which she could draw a modest annuity. The men agreed, and Dolley was told about it. Very gently she rejected the proposal; it would be charity of a sort, she said. She thanked Senator Webster, all her friends, but she could not accept charity.

In 1847 James K. Polk was President, the United States was at war with Mexico — and at last Congress voted to buy the rest of the Madison papers.

President Polk and his wife were devoted admirers of Dolley's. Recently, at a White House levee, Polk had selected her as his partner for the grand promenade, while Mrs. Polk watched, smiling approvingly, as if to say that though other First Ladies might come and go, Mrs. Madison was the First Lady always. It was probably through Polk's knowledge of

Dolley's straits — and of her son Payne's wild extravagances — that a committee was appointed to supervise the transaction of the papers.

Dolley received from Congress five thousand dollars in cash, and twenty thousand dollars more was put in trust to yield her a small regular income. These terms were fair, she thought; but Payne was furious. Shouting his rage, Payne rushed to Washington and threatened the committeemen with a terrible revenge. He said he would take them into court and force them to pay the whole amount of twenty-five thousand dollars immediately. His mother had been grossly insulted. As her sole heir and protector, he would not stand for it!

When Dolley heard of Payne's frenzied behavior, she was appalled, embarrassed — and for once quietly firm. Payne was her adored son. She would never cast him off or publicly admit that he had faults or listen to criticism of him. She would indulge him wherever possible — but not this time! The contract had been signed, she said, the terms would not be altered. He would just have to get over his tantrum.

And then she thrust it all into the background of her thoughts. She was pleased, of course, to have a measure of financial security, the assurance that she might live again in comfort. But there was something else far more important to her.

The Madison papers were now the property of the government; they would be published, read and prized by Americans for as long as the nation existed. She had discharged her duty to dear James. That was what mattered!

On the Fourth of July, 1848, she witnessed the laying of the cornerstone of the splendid monument to George Washington in the city named for him. The morning had been dark and rainy, but by noon the clouds vanished, the sky was a bland and flawless blue. An immense crowd gathered for the historic ceremony. Church bells chimed, flags fluttered, firecrackers snapped and rockets soared.

Dolley sat on the platform erected for the speaker and the guests of honor. She was much interested in the monument. James had been one of its original sponsors, and she herself had helped to raise funds for its construction.

How vividly she remembered George Washington, the first President of the United States — and the other Presidents, too. John Adams, Thomas Jefferson, Madison (the "great little Madison," her Jemmy!) Monroe, John Quincy Adams, Jackson, Van Buren, Harrison, Tyler, Polk — yes, she had known them all. And all, she thought, had been strong in character, courageous and conscientious Chief Executives. This was indeed a marvelous country, never wanting for leaders to hold high the torch of democracy and freedom.

The band played, the veterans of the Mexican War paraded past, and after them came the members of Congress, marching in a body from the Capitol building.

Mrs. Alexander Hamilton had the chair next to Dolley's. "Mrs. Madison," she said, "who is that very tall man among the Representatives? The tallest one, the man with the gaunt, swarthy countenance?"

Dolley leaned forward, the better to see. "It's Mr. Lincoln of Illinois," she answered. "Mr. Abraham Lincoln."

Many people in the crowd were looking up to the platform. "There's Mrs. Madison!" someone said; and Dolley, looking down, saw ladies nodding to her, gentlemen lifting their hats. Smiling, she returned the greetings.

Two weeks ago she had observed her eightieth birthday. "Eighty years old!" she had exclaimed then to Annie Payne. "Just think of it! Why, Annie, I'm an old woman!"

But today, with the sunshine so warm and bright, the music so stirring, and friends around her, she didn't feel old.

Happy, hopeful, still curious about life — really, she felt almost *young*.

BIBLIOGRAPHY

Adams, James Truslow. *History of the United States*. New York: Charles Scribner's Sons, 1933.

Anthony, Katherine. *Dolly Madison, Her Life and Times*. New York: Doubleday and Company, Inc., 1949.

Beveridge, Albert J. *The Life of John Marshall*. Boston: Houghton Mifflin Company, 1916.

Bowers, Claude G. *Jefferson and Hamilton: The Struggle for Democracy*. Boston: Houghton Mifflin Company, 1925.

Bradford, Gamaliel. *Wives*. New York: Harper and Brothers, 1926.

Brant, Irving. *James Madison: The Virginia Revolutionist (1751-1780)*. Indianapolis and New York: The Bobbs-Merrill Company, Inc., 1941.

_____*James Madison: The Nationalist (1780-1787)*. Indianapolis and New York: The Bobbs-Merrill Company, Inc., 1948.

_____*James Madison: Father of the Constitution (1787-1800)*. Indianapolis and New York: The Bobbs-Merrill Company, Inc., 1950.

_____*James Madison: Secretary of State (1800-1809)*. Indianapolis and New York: The Bobbs-Merrill Company, Inc., 1953.

Dean, Elizabeth Lippincott. *Dolly Madison, the Nation's Hostess*. Boston: Lothrop, Lee and Shepard Company, 1928.

Goodwin, Maud Wilder. *Dolly Madison*. New York: Charles Scribner's Sons, 1896.

McConnell, Jane and Bart. *Our First Ladies*. New York: Thomas Y. Crowell Company, 1953.

Nicolay, Helen. *Our Capital on the Potomac*. New York: The Century Company, 1924.

Dictionary of American Biography. Edited by Dumas Malone. New York: Charles Scribner's Sons, 1933.

Encyclopedia of American History. Edited by Richard B. Morris. New York: Harper and Brothers, 1953.

Encyclopaedia Britannica.

INDEX

Dolley Madison

Scotchtown, Hanover County, Virginia, home of the Paynes, description, 13-14; 17, 19, 20, 25, 27, 30, 33, 38, 43, 64

Slavery, attitude of Quakers toward, 14; James Madison's view of, 92, 170

Society of Friends, the, 14; rules, 26, 27; items of discipline, 36, 37; marriage ceremony, 44, 53, 67, 74, 84

Souisatt, Jean Pierre ("French John") 134, 137, 146, 147, 149-155, 157-158, 161, 180

State House in Philadelphia, 42, 48

Tayloe, Benjamin, owner of Octagon House, 160, 164

Tingey, Captain Thomas, 112, 131-132

Todd, John, 41, 44-45, 47-51; marriage to Dolley Payne, 56-57; success as lawyer, 58-60, 63-64, 67, 69, 70; death, 71, 83

Todd, John Payne (son of Dolley Madison) birth, 59, 60-63, 68, 71-74, 83-86, 88, 93-94, 101-102, 110, 119, 123, 137-138, 167-168, 171, 174, 175, 177, 178, 183-185

Todd, William Temple (son of Dolley Madison) 68; death, 71

Tyler, John, becomes President, 181; 186

Tyler, Mrs. Robert, 182

United States Navy, in War of 1812, 141

Van Buren, Martin, President, 179, 181, 186

Virginia, 11, 13, 16, 28, 35, 54, 81

War of 1812, causes, 86-87, 138-139; battles, 141-142; Battle of Bladenburg, 143, 150; Lake Erie, 141-142; the burning of Washington, 156, 159; Fort McHenry, 162-153; Battle of New Orleans, 162

"War Hawks" in Congress, 139, 141

Washington, D. C., establishment and building of, as capital of the United States, 96-97, 99, 107, 115, 119, 120, 128; invaded by British, 142-156, 160-162, 173, 178

Washington, George, 33; at Constitutional Convention, 48, 49; elected first President, 52, 62-63, 67; re-election, 75, 76, 78-79, 87; Farewell Address, 89-90, 96; death, 97, 114; Gilbert Stuart portrait of, 134, 148, 150-152, 166, 185, 186

Washington, George Steptoe, 62-63; marriage to Lucy Payne, 66-68, 71, 72, 94

Washington, Martha, 34, 76-77, 90, 108

Washington Monument, 185, 186

Webster, Daniel, 184

White House, 179; (see President's House)

Williamsburg, Virginia, 14, 24

Wilkinson, General James, in Burr Conspiracy, 125-127

Winder, General William, 143, 158

Yorktown, Battle of, 14